It's another Quality Book from CGP

This book is for anyone doing WJEC Modular GCSE Mathematics at Foundation Level.

Whatever subject you're doing it's the same old story — there are lots of facts and you've just got to learn them. KS4 Maths is no different.

Happily this CGP book gives you all that important information as clearly and concisely as possible.

It's also got some daft bits in to try and make the whole experience at least vaguely entertaining for you.

What CGP is all about

Our sole aim here at CGP is to produce the highest quality books — carefully written, immaculately presented and dangerously close to being funny.

Then we work our socks off to get them out to you — at the cheapest possible prices.

Contents

Published by Coordination Group Publications Ltd.

Written by Richard Parsons

Updated by: Katie Braid, Simon Little, Adam Moorhouse, Julie Wakeling

Proofreading by: Peter Caunter, Paul Jordin

ISBN: 978 1 84762 463 5

Groovy website: www.cgpbooks.co.uk
Printed by Elanders Hindson Ltd, Newcastle upon Tyne.
Jolly bits of clipart from CorelDRAW®

Calculating Tips

Because I'm so lovely, I've come up with some hints and tips for your maths exams.

Always Check the Sign of Numbers in Calculations

It's really important that you check whether numbers are positive or negative when you're doing calculations. Follow these rules:

+	+	makes	+
+	–	makes	–
–	+	makes	–
–	–	makes	+

These rules are only to be used when multiplying or dividing:
e.g. $-2 \times 3 = -6$, $-8 \div -2 = +4$ $-4p \times -2 = +8p$
or when two signs appear next to each other:
e.g. $5 - -4 = 5 + 4 = 9$ $4 + -6 - -7 = 4 - 6 + 7 = 5$

BODMAS

Brackets, Other, Division, Multiplication, Addition, Subtraction

BODMAS tells you the ORDER in which these operations should be done: Work out Brackets first, then Other things like squaring, then Divide / Multiply groups of numbers before Adding or Subtracting them. This set of rules works really well for simple cases, so remember the word BODMAS.

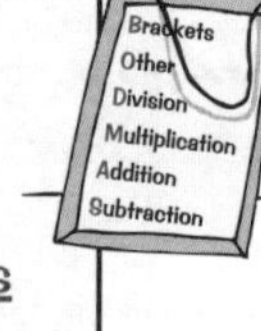

Example: Calculate: $3\times6/-3 + (2 - 6)^2$

Answer: $3\times6/-3 + (2 - 6)^2 = 3\times6/-3 + (-4)^2$
$= 3\times6/-3 + 16$
$= -6 + 16$
$= 10$

Work out the brackets first, then square. Do the multiplications and divisions next before finally adding and subtracting.

There are brackets buttons on your calculator that let you override BODMAS — see page 9

Appropriate Accuracy

When you've got your answer, you need to write it out to an appropriate degree of accuracy — there's no need to keep in all the decimal places on your calculator display. Just remember these three rules:

1) For fairly CASUAL MEASUREMENTS, 2 SIGNIFICANT FIGURES is most appropriate.
   E.g. Cooking — 250g (2 s.f.) of sugar, not 253g (3 s.f.), or 300g (1 s.f.)
   Distance of a journey — 450 miles or 25 miles or 3500 miles (all 2 s.f.)
   Area of a garden or floor — 330 m² or 15 m²
2) For more IMPORTANT OR TECHNICAL THINGS, 3 SIGNIFICANT FIGURES is essential.
   E.g. A technical figure like 34.2 miles per gallon, rather than 34 mpg
   A length that is cut to fit, e.g. measure a shelf 25.6 cm long not just 26 cm
   Any accurate measurement with a ruler: 67.5 cm not 70 cm or 67.54 cm
3) Only for REALLY SCIENTIFIC WORK would you have more than 3 SIG. FIG.

For more on rounding, see p.6-7.

BUT: this is only for when you're writing out your final answer. If your calculation involves loads of stages, don't round off until the end — this will mean that your final answer is more accurate.

For example: "James is putting new carpets in two of his rooms. One room measures 3.56 m by 2.96 m. The second room measures 4.52 m by 3.73 m. How much carpet does James need to buy?"

$3.56 \times 2.96 = 10.5376\ m^2$
$4.52 \times 3.73 = 16.8596\ m^2$
$10.5376 + 16.8596 = 27.3972\ m^2$ — Keep all the decimal places during this stage of the calculation...
$= \underline{27.4\ m^2}$ — ...then round off the final answer.

Calculating Tips

Make Sure You Include the Units

This is probably pretty obvious, but it's an easy thing to forget in the exam so...

ALWAYS CHECK WHETHER YOUR ANSWER NEEDS A UNIT

The question might already say what units the answer needs to be in, or you might need to work it out:

> For example, if it's a question about area, and the measurements are given in cm, then your answer will need to be given as cm^2.
> Or, if it's a question about volume, and the measurements are given in m, then your answer will need to be given as m^3.

The units could also affect how you need to write out your answer...

If your calculator reads [3.6], think before you merrily jot down 3.6 as your answer. 3.6 what? Pipers piping? It sounds silly, but it can lose you easy marks in the exam. E.g. If you're answering a money question, £3.6 won't get you any marks — you need to write £3.60.

Don't Be Scared of Wordy Questions

About a third of the marks on your exam come from wordy, real-life questions. For these you don't just have to do the maths, you've got to work out what the question's asking you to do first. Relax and work through them step by step.

1) READ the question carefully. Work out what bit of maths you need to answer it.
2) Underline the INFORMATION YOU NEED to answer the question — you might not have to use all the numbers they give you.
3) Write out the question IN MATHS and answer it, showing all your working clearly.

Example:

> A return car journey from Carlisle to Manchester uses 4/7 of a tank of petrol.
> It costs £56 for a full tank of petrol.
> How much does the journey cost?

1) The "4/7" tells you this is a fractions question.
2) You need £56 (the cost of a full tank) and 4/7 (the fraction of the tank used).
3) You want to know 4/7 of £56, so in maths:

£56 × 4/7 = £32

It doesn't matter where they're driving from and to.

Don't forget the units in your final answer — this is a question about cost in pounds, so the units will be £.

Remember to ALWAYS SHOW YOUR WORKING — this way you may still pick up marks even if you make a mistake with the final answer.

Always Check Your Answer

It's always a good idea to check your answers by working backwards through your calculations.

That way you can pick up any silly mistakes you might have made.

Example: If $y = 2x^2 + 3$, find the value of y when x = 3.

Answer: $y = 2 \times (3)^2 + 3$
$= 2 \times 9 + 3$
$= 18 + 3$
$= 21$

Check: $21 - 3 = 18$
$18 \div 2 = 9$
$\sqrt{9} = 3$

Hurray — you've got the same number you started with.

Big Numbers

Here's a nice easy page to get you going. You need to be able to:

1) Read big numbers E.g. how would you say 1 734 564?
2) Write them down E.g. write 'Thirty-two thousand and three' as a number.
3) Put them in order of size E.g. put 10 646 9853 79 in ascending order.

Always Look at Big Numbers in Groups of Three

1) Always start from the extreme right-hand side of the number →
2) Moving left, ←, put a space in every 3 digits to break it up into groups of 3.
3) Now going right, →, read each group of three as a separate number and add 'million' and 'thousand' on for the first two groups (assuming 3 groups in all).

2 351 243

So many MILLION So many THOUSAND And the rest

(i.e. 2 million, 351 thousand, 243) or written fully in words:
Two million, three hundred and fifty-one thousand, two hundred and forty-three.

Putting Numbers in Order of Size

Example: 12 84 623 32 486 4563 75 2143

① It may not be exactly difficult, but it's still best to do it in two steps. First put them into groups, the ones with fewest digits first:

(all the 2-digit ones, then all the 3-digit ones, then all the 4-digit ones etc.)
12 84 32 75 | 623 486 | 4563 2143

② Then just put each separate group in order of size:

12 32 75 84 | 486 623 | 2143 4563

Hint: Don't call numbers big or small to their face — they're very sensitive...

There's nothing too tricky about putting numbers into order of size — just remember the tips above. In fact, you might even find it strangely satisfying. A bit like alphabetising your CD collection.

1) Write these numbers in words: a) 1 234 531 b) 23 456 c) 2415 d) 3402 e) 203 412
2) Write this down as a number: Fifty-six thousand, four hundred and twenty-one
3) Put these numbers in order of size: 23 493 87 1029 3004 345 9
4) Write these numbers in ascending order: 37 8 307 9 2

Negative Numbers and Temperature

Negative numbers can be tricky little blighters to put in the correct order — this page'll show you how to get them in line — in a number line that is...

The Number Line

You need to remember the diagram of THE NUMBER LINE as shown to the right — it could be the answer to all your problems — well, all your negative number problems anyway.

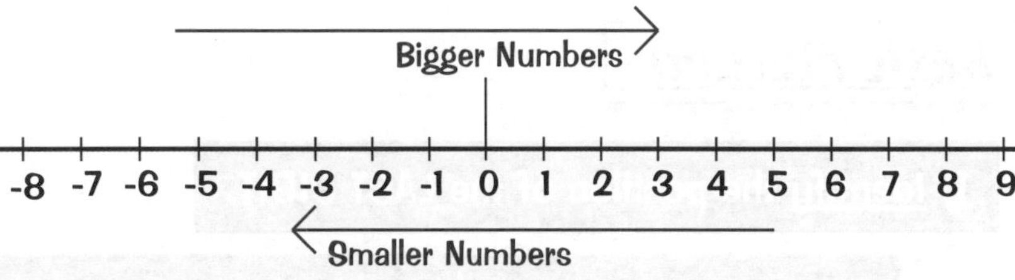

1) Putting Negative Numbers in Order

EXAMPLE: Put these numbers in order: 12, -4, 5, -2, 10, -11, 2, -7

ANSWER: 1) Quickly draw out the full Number Line as shown below

2) Put the numbers in the same order as they appear on the number line.

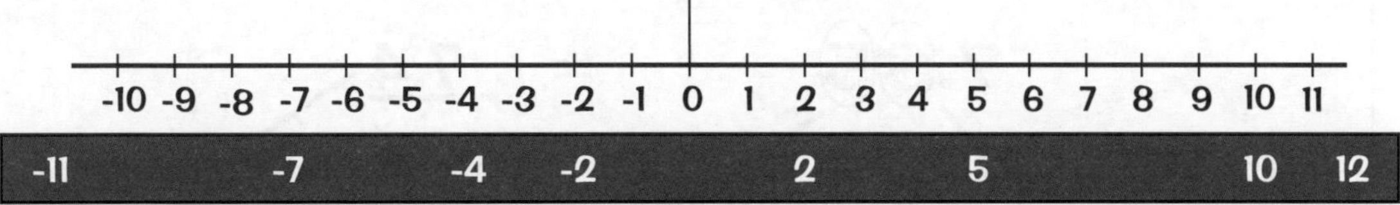

So in order of size they are: -11, -7, -4, -2, 2, 5, 10, 12

Note that -4 is BIGGER than -7, because it is FURTHER UP THE NUMBER LINE.
Negative numbers go the "wrong way" — smaller numbers are bigger!

2) Finding The Range of Values

A very common Exam question is for the RANGE OF TEMPERATURE for a place where it goes below freezing at night.

EXAMPLE: One day the temperatures in Moscow were: Midday 7 °C, Midnight -15 °C
What was the full RANGE of temperature?

ANSWER: Once again, just do a quick sketch of the Number Line, mark the two temperatures on it and then just count how many degrees it is between them — easy:

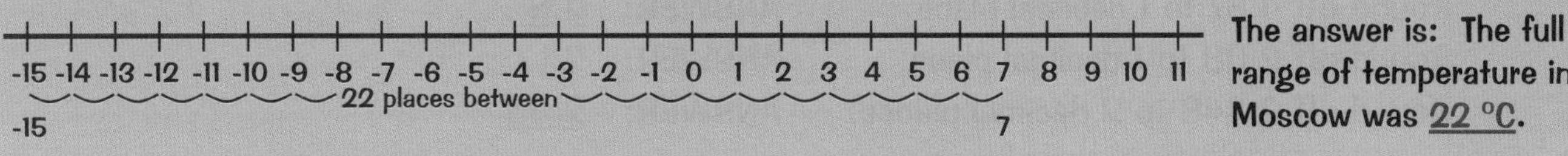

The answer is: The full range of temperature in Moscow was 22 °C.

You can also calculate the range by subtracting the smallest number from the biggest number.
If one or both of the numbers are negative, you'll have to use one of these rules:

+ +	makes	+	+ –	makes	–
– +	makes	–	– –	makes	+

So in the example above the range is: 7 – -15 = 7 + 15 = 22

Rounding Off

When you have decimal numbers you might have to round them off to the nearest whole number. The trouble is, they could also ask you to round them off to one decimal place (or possibly two decimal places). This isn't too bad but you do have to learn some rules for it:

Basic Method

1) Identify the position of the LAST DIGIT.

2) Then look at the next digit to the right – called the DECIDER.

3) If the DECIDER is 5 or more, then ROUND-UP the LAST DIGIT.
If the DECIDER is 4 or less, then leave the LAST DIGIT as it is.

EXAMPLE: What is 7.35 to 1 Decimal Place?

7.35 = 7.4

LAST DIGIT to be written (because we're rounding to 1 Decimal Place)

DECIDER

The LAST DIGIT ROUNDS UP to 4 because the DECIDER is 5 or more

Decimal Places (D.P.)

1) To round off to ONE DECIMAL PLACE, the LAST DIGIT will be the one just after the decimal point.

2) There must be NO MORE DIGITS after the LAST DIGIT (not even zeros).

EXAMPLES

Round off 2.34 to 1 decimal place. ANSWER: 2.3
Round off 4.57 to 1 decimal place. ANSWER: 4.6
Round off 2.08 to 1 decimal place. ANSWER: 2.1
Round off 2.346 to 2 decimal places. ANSWER: 2.35

Rounding off decimal places — I totally dig it...

Personally, I quite like the rounding off methods on this page. They make it easier to explain to my numbers why I've rounded them up or down — I just blame the rules. They take it less personally then.

1) Round these numbers off to 1 decimal place:
a) 3.24 b) 1.78 c) 2.31 d) 0.46 e) 9.76

2) Round these off to 2 decimal place:
a) 3.465 b) 5.278 c) 1.844 d) 6.955 e) 3.267

Rounding Off

If you thought that it was only numbers with decimal places that could be rounded off — then you're wrong. So very, very wrong. Whole numbers can be rounded off too. Yay.

Rounding Whole Numbers

The easiest ways to round off a number are:

1) 'To the nearest WHOLE NUMBER'
2) 'To the nearest TEN'
3) 'To the nearest HUNDRED'
4) 'To the nearest THOUSAND'

This isn't difficult so long as you remember the 2 RULES:

> 1) The number always lies between 2 POSSIBLE ANSWERS, just choose the one it's NEAREST TO.
> 2) If the number is exactly in the MIDDLE, then ROUND IT UP.

EXAMPLES:

1) Give 231 to the nearest TEN.
ANSWER: 231 is between 230 and 240, but it is nearer to 230

2) Round 45.7 to the nearest WHOLE NUMBER.
ANSWER: 45.7 is between 45 and 46, but it is nearer to 46

Significant Figures (S.F.)

The method for significant figures is identical to that for decimal places except that finding the position of the LAST DIGIT is more difficult — it wouldn't be so bad, but for the ZEROS...

> 1) The 1st significant figure of any number is simply THE FIRST DIGIT WHICH ISN'T A ZERO.

> 2) The 2nd, 3rd, 4th, etc. significant figures follow on immediately after the 1st, REGARDLESS OF BEING ZEROS OR NOT ZEROS.

E.g 0.002309 — SIG FIGS: 1st 2nd 3rd 4th

2.03070 — SIG FIGS: 1st 2nd 3rd 4th

(If we're rounding to say, 3 s.f., then the LAST DIGIT is simply the 3rd sig. fig.)

> 3) After Rounding Off the LAST DIGIT, end ZEROS must be filled in up to, BUT NOT BEYOND, the decimal point.

No extra zeros must ever be put in after the decimal point.

Examples	to 4 s.f.	to 3 s.f.	to 2 s.f.	to 1 s.f.
1) 54.7651	54.77	54.8	55	50
2) 17.0067	17.01	17.0	17	20

Exam cheat wish #23 — all marks are rounded up to the nearest 100%...

Learn the 2 Rules for Rounding Whole Numbers and the 3 Extra Rules about Significant Figures. Simples.

1) Round these off to the nearest 10:
a) 453 b) 682 c) 46.2 d) 98 e) 14

2) Round these numbers to the stated no. of significant figures:
a) 352 to 2 s.f. b) 465 to 1 s.f. c) 12.38 to 3 s.f. d) 0.03567 to 2 s.f.

Calculator Buttons

In Unit 1 and Unit 3 you'll be allowed to use a calculator — so it's really important that you get to know your calculator before the exam. You could take it out for dinner and find out about its hobbies. But it might be more useful to work through the next two pages with your own calculator to see where all the buttons are — not all calculators are the same.

The FRACTION BUTTON [a b/c]

You do need to know how to deal with fractions without your calculator.
But when you're allowed to use it, you definitely should do...

1) TO ENTER A NORMAL FRACTION like $\frac{1}{4}$

Just press: [1] [a b/c] [4]

DISCLAIMER
The buttons on this page are merely an artist's interpretation of the buttons featured on an actual calculator — pressing them will have little or no effect.

2) TO ENTER A MIXED FRACTION like $1\frac{3}{5}$

Just press: [1] [a b/c] [3] [a b/c] [5]

3) TO DO A REGULAR CALCULATION such as $\frac{1}{5} \times \frac{3}{4}$

Just press: [1] [a b/c] [5] [×] [3] [a b/c] [4] [=]

4) TO REDUCE A FRACTION TO ITS LOWEST TERMS

Just enter it and then press [=].

e.g., [9] [a b/c] [12] [=] → 3⌟4 $= \frac{3}{4}$

5) TO CONVERT BETWEEN MIXED AND TOP HEAVY FRACTIONS

Just press [SHIFT] [a b/c] e.g. to give $2\frac{3}{8}$ as a top heavy fraction:

Press: [2] [a b/c] [3] [a b/c] [8] [=] [SHIFT] [a b/c] which gives an answer of $\frac{19}{8}$.

The MEMORY BUTTONS — [STO] Store, [RCL] Recall

These are really useful for keeping a number you've just calculated, so you can use it again shortly afterwards.

EXAMPLE: Find $\frac{840}{15 + 5^3}$ — just work out the bottom line first and stick it in the memory.

So press [15] [+] [5] [x³] [=] and then [STO] [M] to keep the result of the bottom line in the memory.
Then you simply press [840] [÷] [RCL] [M] [=], and the answer is 6.

The memory buttons might work a bit differently on your calculator. Note, if your calculator has an 'Ans' button, you can do the same thing as above using that instead — the Ans button gives you the result you got when you last pressed the '=' button.

Calculator Buttons

BODMAS and the BRACKETS BUTTONS (and)

Calculators work things out in a certain order (BODMAS — see p.2). So for simple things like $\frac{23+45}{64\times3}$ you can't just press 23 + 45 ÷ 64 × 3 = — it will be completely wrong.
The calculator will think you mean $23+\frac{45}{64}\times3$ because the calculator will do the division and multiplication BEFORE it does the addition.

The secret is to OVERRIDE the automatic BODMAS order of operations using the BRACKETS BUTTONS. Brackets are the ultimate priority in BODMAS, which means anything in brackets is worked out before anything else happens to it.

So all you have to do is:

1) Write a couple of pairs of brackets into the expression: $\frac{(23+45)}{(64\times3)}$
2) Then just type it as it's written:

(23 + 45) ÷ (64 × 3) =

You might think it's difficult to know where to put the brackets in.
It's not that difficult, you just put them in pairs around each group of numbers.
It's OK to have brackets within other brackets too, e.g. (4 + (5÷2)).
As a rule, you can't cause trouble by putting too many brackets in,

SO LONG AS THEY ALWAYS GO IN PAIRS.

Your Calculator Has a Square Button

Okay, so all the buttons are square, but I'm talking about this button, x^2, for squaring numbers.

It also has a square root button, √.

To calculate 7 squared, press: 7 x^2 = ...you should get 49.

To calculate the square root of 49, press: √ 4 9 = ...you should get 7.

The Powers Button — x^y or ^

See p.50-51 for more on powers and roots.

It's used for working out powers of numbers quickly. For example to find 7^5, instead of pressing 7 × 7 × 7 × 7 × 7, you should just press 7 x^y 5 = .

There is also the root button, $\sqrt[y]{\ }$. To calculate the cube root of 64, press: 3 $\sqrt[y]{\ }$ 6 4 = .

Learn these two pages, store, then recall...

Remember to practise everything you've just learnt on these two pages on your own calculator.

1) Calculate the following to 2 d.p. using the brackets or memory buttons:

a) $\frac{15+5^6}{21^3-4^3}$ b) $\frac{74^2-10^3}{\sqrt{49}\times2^4}$

Fractions, Decimals, Percentages and Ratios

Big title huh? — But don't be worried, because these four types of number have one thing in common — they all show proportions of things.

Fractions, decimals and percentages are simply three different ways of expressing a proportion of something — and it's pretty important you should see them as closely related and completely interchangeable with each other. This table shows the really common conversions which you should know straight off without having to work them out:

Fraction	Decimal	Percentage
1/2	0.5	50%
1/4	0.25	25%
3/4	0.75	75%
1/3	0.333333... or $0.\dot{3}$	$33\frac{1}{3}$%
2/3	0.666666.... or $0.\dot{6}$	$66\frac{2}{3}$%
1/10	0.1	10%
2/10	0.2	20%
X/10	0.X	X0%
1/5	0.2	20%
2/5	0.4	40%

⅓ and ⅔ have what're known as 'recurring' decimals — the same pattern of numbers carries on repeating itself forever. (Except here, the pattern's just a single 3 or a single 6. You could have, for instance: 0.143143143...)

Ratios Show the Relative Amounts of Things

A RATIO describes how something is divided up — if the ratio of red to green balls is 1:2, there are only half as many red balls as green balls.
This means that the whole grisly subject of RATIOS gets a whole lot easier when you do this:

Turn RATIOS into FRACTIONS

What the fraction form of the ratio actually means

1) Suppose in a class there are girls and boys in the ratio 3 : 4.
This means there are $\frac{3}{4}$ as many girls as boys.
2) So if there were 20 boys, there would be $\frac{3}{4} \times 20 = 15$ girls.
You've got to be careful though — it doesn't mean $\frac{3}{4}$ of the people in the class are girls.
In fact, three sevenths of the class are girls.

Oh, what's recurrin'?...

Knowing all of the top table and how to treat ratios will speed you up nicely in exams.

1) Convert the following numbers: a) convert $\frac{3}{10}$ to a decimal. b) convert 80% to a fraction.

Fractions

This page covers all the basics to help you deal with those pesky fractions.
You need to make sure that you can do everything explained here. Every last smidgen.

Finding a Fraction of Something — just multiply

Multiply the 'something' by the TOP of the fraction, then divide it by the BOTTOM:

E.g. "Find $\frac{9}{20}$ of £360." 'Of' just means multiply.

$\frac{9}{20}$ of £360 = $\{(9) \times £360\} \div (20) = \frac{£3240}{20} = £162$

or: $\frac{9}{20}$ of £360 = $\frac{9}{1} \times £360 \times \frac{1}{20} = £162$

You can do this QUICKLY on your calculator using the fraction key — see page 8

Fractional Changes — Finding the New Value of Things

To answer these just work out the fraction of the ORIGINAL AMOUNT as above and then either ADD or SUBTRACT this from the original amount to get the new amount.

E.g. "A T-shirt that usually costs £20 is reduced by a quarter in a sale. What is the new price?"

Reduction is $\frac{1}{4} \times £20 = \{(1) \times £20\} \div 4 = £5$

So new price is £20 - £5 = £15

Equivalent Fractions

Equivalent fractions are fractions that are equal in value, even though they look different.
Starting with any fraction you like, you can make up a list of equivalent fractions by simply MULTIPLYING top and bottom by the SAME NUMBER each time:

$\frac{1}{2} = \frac{3}{6}$ (×3 top and bottom) $\quad \frac{3}{4} = \frac{15}{20}$ (×5 top and bottom) $\quad \frac{1}{5} = \frac{100}{500}$ (×100 top and bottom)

Expressing One Number as a Fraction of Another

This is dead easy — you just put the 'one number' over the other number.

E.g. 'There are 33 pupils in class 11S. 22 of them are girls. Express this as a fraction'

Answer: $\frac{22}{33}$. This fraction can be simplified by 'cancelling down' (dividing top and bottom by the same number) to give an answer of $\frac{2}{3}$.

$\frac{22}{33} = \frac{2}{3}$ (÷11 top and bottom)

No fractions were harmed in the making of this page...

Now you've learnt this page, it's time to have a go at these below.

1) a) Find $\frac{2}{5}$ of 550. b) What's $\frac{7}{8}$ of £2? c) In a $\frac{3}{4}$ off sale what's the new price of a £20 shirt?

Percentages

These two pages are all about percentages in real-life situations. It's a thinly veiled attempt by examiners to make maths more 'relevant'. So let's humour them — it's bound to be in the exam.

Two Important Details:

Make sure you remember them!

1) 'Per cent' means 'out of 100' so 20% means '20 out of 100' = $20 \div 100 = \frac{20}{100}$
2) 'OF' means '×'. In maths, the word 'of' can always be replaced with '×' for working out the answer. (as shown in the method below)

Finding a Percentage of a Quantity is Simple

MOST percentage questions are like this: **Work out 'something %' of 'something else'.**

E.g. "Find 20% of £60."

This is the method to use:

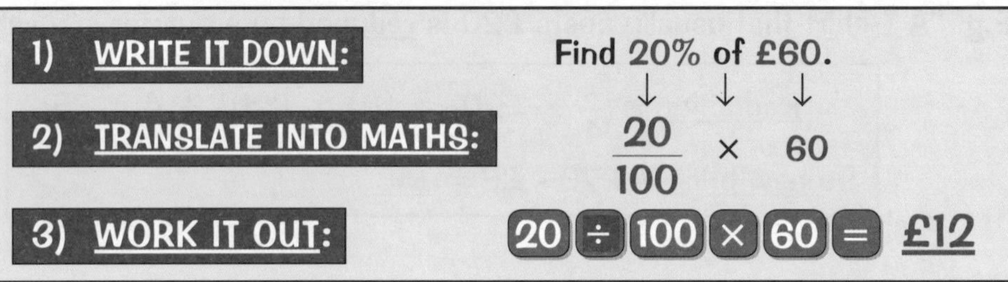

Percentage Changes — Find the Percentage First

PERCENTAGE CHANGES can also be worked out using the SAME BASIC METHOD above.
You just work out the percentage first, and then add or subtract this from the original amount.
These questions are often asked in the form of % DISCOUNT, or ADDED TAX (e.g. VAT).

E.g. A radio is priced at £8.50 but there is a discount of 20% available.
FIND THE REDUCED PRICE OF THE RADIO.

ANSWER:
First find 20% of £8.50:

1) 20% of £8.50
2) $\frac{20}{100} \times 8.5$
3) 20 ÷ 100 × 8.5 = 1.7 = £1.70

It's money, so 1.7 on the calculator display is £1.70.

This is the DISCOUNT so we take it away to get the final answer: £8.50 – £1.70 = £6.80

If you are asked to calculate a price including TAX (e.g. VAT), remember that the price will INCREASE. So use the method above to work out the percentage, and then ADD this to the ORIGINAL AMOUNT.

Percentages

In an exam you might be asked to compare two numbers using percentages. Wowsers.

Comparing Numbers using Percentages

This is the other common type of percentage question.

Give 'one number' AS A PERCENTAGE OF 'another number'

For example, "Express £2 as a percentage of £20." This is the method to use:

The FDP Method:

Fraction		Decimal		Percentage
$\frac{2}{20}$	$2 \div 20$ →	0.1	$\times 100$ →	10%
First make a FRACTION out of the 2 numbers, always with the smaller number on top.		DIVIDE them to get a DECIMAL.		Then multiply by 100 to get a PERCENTAGE.

Two Important Examples

1) "A shopkeeper buys pens at 8p each and sells them for 10p each. What is his PERCENTAGE PROFIT?"

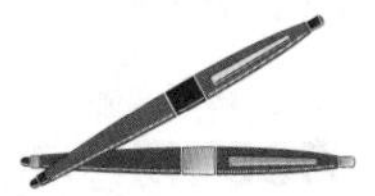

Answer: The two numbers we want to compare are the PROFIT (which is 2p) with the ORIGINAL cost (which is 8p). We then apply the FDP method:

Fraction → Decimal → Percentage:
$\frac{2}{8}$ → 0.25 → 25%

so the shopkeeper makes a 25% profit on the pens.

2) "In a sale, a tennis racket is bought for £60 and then sold for £48. What PERCENTAGE LOSS is this?"

It's a loss as the item is sold for less than it was bought...

Answer:
The two numbers we want to compare are the REDUCTION (which is £12) and the ORIGINAL VALUE (which is £60). We then apply the FDP method:

Fraction → Decimal → Percentage:
$\frac{12}{60}$ → 0.2 → 20%

63% of all statistics are made up...

So, the 'ole FDP method comes in handy here too. Time to check what you've learnt from this page...

1) A house increases in value from £140 000 to £182 000.
What is the increase in value of the house as a percentage?

Percentage Problems and Money

This page shows you how to deal with repeated percentage changes. They crop up in things like compound interest and tell you how the value of your car is decreasing and decreasing...

Repeated Percentage Increase and Decrease Problems

For example: "Ali buys a really big potato for £800. The value of her potato depreciates by 25% each year. Find the value of Ali's potato after 3 years."

Value after 1 year is: £800 × 0.75 = £600
Value after 2 years is: £600 × 0.75 = £450
Value after 3 years is: £450 × 0.75 = £337.50

A depreciation of 25% means a percentage decrease of 25%. So you need to work out 100 − 25 = 75% of the original value. 75% as a decimal is 0.75.

So you're basically just multiplying by 0.75 for each year. A quicker way of setting this out would be: £800 × 0.75 × 0.75 × 0.75, or even better: £800 × 0.75^3.

There's a Formula for Repeated Percentage Changes

If you want to you can use this formula to work out repeated percentage change problems:

$$N = N_0(1 + r/100)^n$$

- N — Existing amount at this time
- N_0 — Initial amount
- r — Percentage change per day/hour/year
- n — Number of days/hrs/yrs

The (1+ r/100) bit might look a bit confusing in the formula but in practise it's really easy:

E.g. For a 5% INCREASE (1+ r/100) = (1 + 5/100) = (1+ 0.05) = 1.05

For a 5% DECREASE (1+ r/100) = (1 + -5/100) = (1 − 0.05) = 0.95

E.g. "A man invests £1000 in a savings account which pays 8% compound interest per year. How much will there be after 6 years?"

ANSWER: Amount = $1000(1.08)^6$ = £1586.87

(1000 = Initial amount, 1.08 = 8% increase, 6 = 6 years)

An increase in the value of something is called appreciation.

This is an example of a COMPOUND INTEREST problem — the value of something is increasing by a certain percentage each year.

Simple Interest is Different — It's a Bit Simpler...

In simple interest the value increases by the SAME AMOUNT OF MONEY each year.

E.g. "A man invests £1000 in a savings account which pays 8% SIMPLE interest per year. How much will there be after 6 years?"

ANSWER: First of all work out the amount of money paid in interest each year:

£1000 × 8% = £1000 × (8/100) = £80

Then multiply this amount by the number of years to get the total interest:

£80 × 6 = £480.

Finally, add the interest and the initial amount together: £1000 + £480 = £1480

Percentage Problems and Money

I simply must have that new J-BS album... but I don't have the moolah... Sound familiar? This page may help you out. It's all about finding the best buy, paying bills and hire purchase...

A favourite type of question they like to ask you in Exams is comparing the 'value for money' of 2 or 3 similar items. Always follow the GOLDEN RULE...

Divide by the PRICE in pence (to get the amount per penny)

E.g. The local 'Supplies 'n' Vittals' stocks three sizes of Jamaican Gooseberry Jam. The question is: Which of these represents 'THE BEST VALUE FOR MONEY'?

500 g at £1.08   350 g at 80p   100 g at 42p

ANSWER: the GOLDEN RULE says: Divide the price in pence to get the amount per penny.

500 g ÷ 108p = 4.6 g PER PENNY

350 g ÷ 80p = 4.4 g PER PENNY

100 g ÷ 42p = 2.4 g PER PENNY

So you can now see straight away that THE 500 g JAR is the best value for money because you get MORE JAM PER PENNY.

You Can Work Out Bills With Simple Calculations...

You may need to use your knowledge of percentages to answer questions on bills.
EXAMPLE: "Find the total cost of the electricity including VAT from the bill given below."

Previous meter reading	1654
New meter reading	2148
Price per unit (in pence)	12.5
Service Charge	£22.50
VAT at 5% of total charge	

ANSWER: Go through the bill step by step.

1) Find the number of units used (the difference): 2148 - 1654 = 494
2) Multiply the number of units by the price per unit: 494 × 12.5 = 6175p = £61.75
3) Add the service charge: 61.75 + 22.50 = £84.25
4) Work out the VAT (see p.12) and add it to the total to get the final bill:

5% of £84.25 = $\frac{5}{100}$ × 84.25 = £4.21. So the total cost is: 84.25 + 4.21 = £88.46

A Hire Purchase Includes a Deposit and Monthly Payments

You can sometimes buy things on hire purchase. This means you pay an initial deposit and then make regular payments over a set period of time.

E.g. "The cash price of a car is £12 000. It can be bought on hire purchase for a 15% deposit and 36 monthly payments of £320. What is the hire purchase price?"

ANSWER: Deposit: $\frac{15}{100}$ × 12 000 = £1800. Monthly payments: 320 × 36 = £11 520
So the hire purchase price is: £1800 + £11 520 = £13 320

Substituting Numbers into Formulas

This page shows you how to perform the magical transformation of sentences into mathematical formulas. Brace yourself — this page will change the way you look at pricing... forever...

Example 1:

The rates of a bike rental service are given below:

COST PER BIKE = NUMBER OF HOURS × £2 + DELIVERY CHARGE

What does it cost to hire two bikes for 24 hours when the delivery charge is £10?

ANSWER:
Simply substitute the information given in the question into the formula and then do the calculation — but **REMEMBER TO USE BODMAS.**

Number of hours = 24. Delivery charge = £10

1) First substitute these numbers into the equation:
   COST PER BIKE = 24 × £2 + £10
2) Then work it out in stages using BODMAS (see p.2)
   (In this case Multiplication before Addition)
   COST PER BIKE = £48 + £10 = £58
3) You need the price for two bikes so multiply this number by 2 to get the total cost:
   TOTAL COST = 2 × £58 = £116

Example 2:

Dave earns £10 per hour and every week he gets a bonus of £20. If Dave works for 25 hours a week, how much does he earn in total for one week?

ANSWER:
This question is a bit trickier as you have to create a formula. **BUT DON'T PANIC.**

1) Firstly write down all the contributions to Dave's earnings:
   He earns £10 per hour. So that's £10 × number of hours worked
   He also gets a weekly bonus of £20
2) So TOTAL EARNINGS = £10 × number of hours + £20
   Then work it out in stages using BODMAS.
   TOTAL EARNINGS = £10 × 25 + £20 = £250 + £20 = £270

I'll pay you £1 per page and £10 when you finish this book...

That's a lie. You won't get any money from me but you will have the priceless ability to answer this question:

1) The cost of hiring a DVD is £3 per night, but new members have to pay a joining fee of £5. How much does it cost a new member to rent a DVD for 3 nights?

Formula Triangles and Speed

Formula triangles are extremely useful tools for lots of tricky maths problems.
They're very easy to use and very easy to remember. But don't just take my word for it...

If 3 things are related by a formula that looks either

like this: $A = B \times C$ or like this: $B = \frac{A}{C}$

then you can put them into a FORMULA TRIANGLE like this:

1) First decide where the letters go:

1) If there are TWO LETTERS MULTIPLIED TOGETHER in the formula then they must go ON THE BOTTOM of the Formula Triangle (and so the other one must go on the top).

   For example the formula '$F = m \times a$' fits into a formula triangle like this

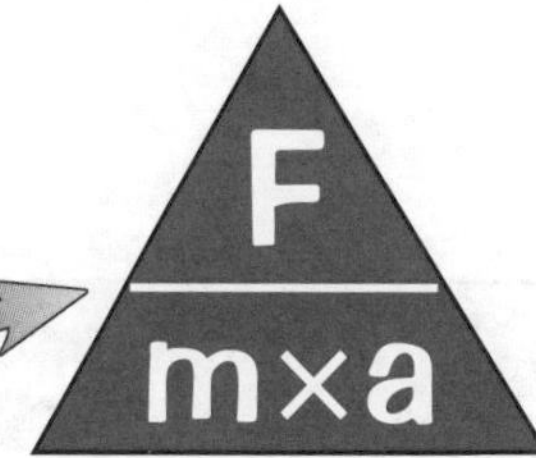

2) If there's ONE THING DIVIDED BY ANOTHER in the formula then the one ON TOP OF THE DIVISION goes ON TOP IN THE FORMULA TRIANGLE (and so the other two must go on the bottom — it doesn't matter which way round).

   So the formula 'Speed = Distance / Time' fits into a formula triangle like this.

2) Using the Formula Triangle:

Once you've got the formula triangle sorted out, the rest is easy:

1) COVER UP the thing you want to find and just WRITE DOWN what's left showing.
2) PUT IN THE VALUES for the other two things and just WORK IT OUT.

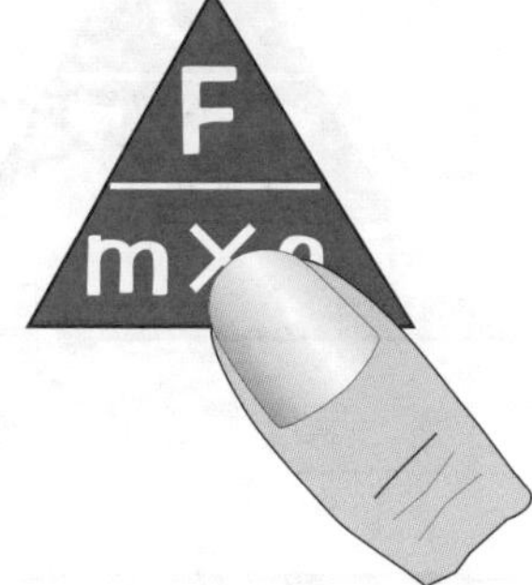

EXAMPLE:
"Using $F = m \times a$, find the value of 'a' when $F = 20$ and $m = 50$"

ANSWER: Using the formula triangle, we want to find 'a' so we cover 'a' up, and that leaves 'F/m' showing (i.e. $F \div m$).
So '$a = F/m$', and putting the numbers in we get: $a = 20/50 = 0.4$

Formula triangles — it's all a big cover up...

By now, you should be convinced that formula triangles are the most amazingly useful thing ever. They'll help make using formulas much easier. The best thing to do is learn the whole page, cover it up and scribble down everything you can remember. It's a really good way to help you learn everything.

Formula Triangles and Speed

I know, I know. This is Maths, but you do have to know a bit of Physics in case it comes up in your exam. Sorry, but that's the way the cookie crumbles.

Speed = Distance ÷ Time

This is very common. In fact it probably comes up every single year — and they never give you the formula. Either learn it beforehand or wave goodbye to lots of easy marks.
Life isn't all bad though — there's an easy FORMULA TRIANGLE:

Of course you still have to remember the order of the letters in the triangle (S^DT) — but this time we have the word SoDiT to help you.
So if it's a question on speed, distance and time just say: **SOD IT**.

EXAMPLE:

"A car travels 90 miles at 36 miles per hour. How long does it take?"

ANSWER: We want to find the TIME, so cover up T in the triangle which leaves D/S,

so T = D/S = Distance ÷ speed = 90÷36 = 2.5 hours

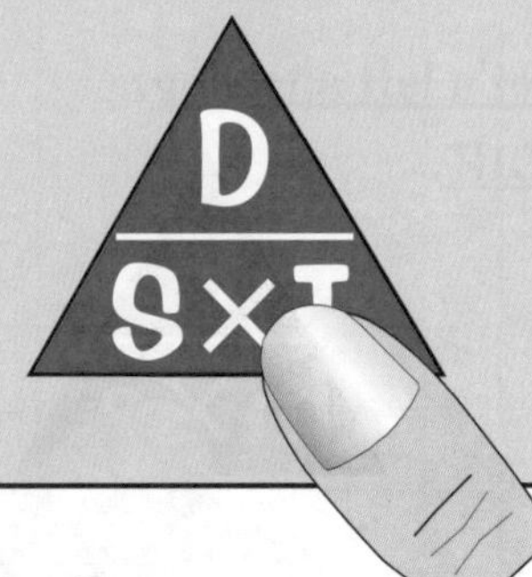

LEARN THE FORMULA TRIANGLE, AND YOU'LL FIND QUESTIONS ON SPEED, DISTANCE AND TIME VERY EASY.

Formula for success — always butter your bread on the right side...

Learn the formula for speed, and also the Formula triangle. Then have a go at these:

1) What's the formula for speed, distance and time?
2) Find the time taken, for a person walking at 3.2 km/h to cover 24 km.
   Also, find how far she'll walk in 3 hrs 30 mins.

Interpreting Graphs

Time to look at interpreting some graphs now — that's the plot of this page...

Conversion Graphs

These are really easy. In the Exam you're likely to get a Conversion Graph question which converts between things like £ → Dollars or mph → km/h, etc.

This graph converts between miles and kilometres

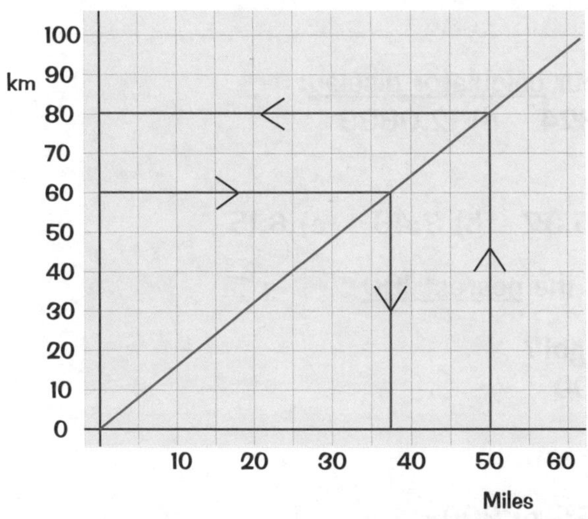

2 very typical questions:

1) How many miles is 60 km?

ANS: Draw a line straight across from '60' on the 'km' axis 'til it hits the line, then go straight down to the 'miles' axis and read off the answer: 37.5 miles

2) How many km is 50 miles?

ANS: Draw a line straight up from '50' on the 'miles' axis 'til it hits the line, then go straight across to the 'km' axis and read off the answer: 80 km

METHOD:

1) Draw a line from the value on one axis.
2) Keep going 'til you hit the LINE.
3) Then change direction and go straight to the other axis.
4) Read off the new value from the axis. That's the answer.

Interpreting Graphs

You could be asked to interpret graphs showing information on all kinds of situations.

Example: "The graph shows the height of a ball as it is thrown through the air. Use the graph to find the approximate times when the ball was 1 m above the ground."

Method:

Draw a straight line across the graph at 1.0 on the y axis — this is where the height of the ball is 1 m.

The curve crosses this line twice. Draw lines down to the x axis at these points and read off the values:

Time = 0.2 s and 0.6 s.

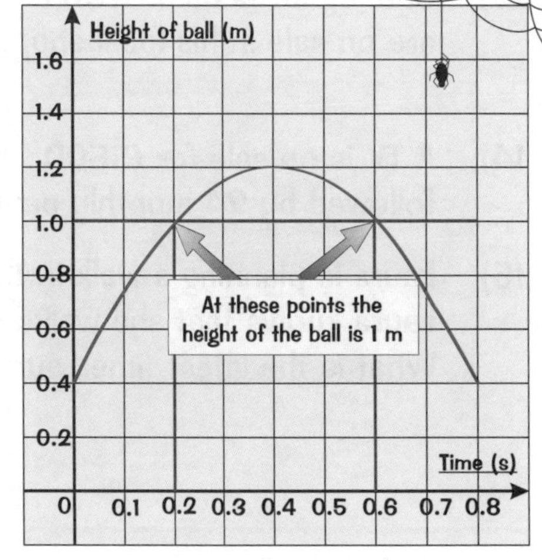

Right graph — we're not leaving here 'til I get some answers...

Learn all the stuff on this lovely page. Every last bit of it.
Then turn over... bla bla bla ... you know what to do...

Revision Summary for Unit One — 1

WHAT YOU'RE SUPPOSED TO DO HERE is put all the methods from the first half of Section One into practice to answer these questions.

1) Write this number out in words: 21 306 515

2) Put these numbers in order of size:
a) 23 6534 123 2200 2 132 789 45
b) -2, 4, 0, -7, -6, 10, 8, 5

3) These are the sort of numbers you might get in your calculator display:
a) 1.2343534 b) 2.9999999 c) 15.534624 d) 12.0833
Round them off to the nearest whole number.

4) Round these numbers off to 1 decimal place: a) 5.32 b) 3.46 c) 6.15

5) a) Give 246 to the nearest 10 b) Give 860 to the nearest 100

6) How many significant figures have these numbers got?
a) 12 b) 150 c) 2000 d) 23.4 e) 8500

7) Use the a^b_c button to reduce $12/15$ to its simplest form.

8) Calculate a) 4/7 of 560 b) 2/5 of £150 c) 65% of 300

9) A DVD player costs £50 plus VAT. If VAT is 17.5%, how much does the DVD player cost?

10) Carl has £35 to spend. He wants to use a 20%-off voucher to buy a top that should cost £45. Can he afford the top?

11) Joe wants to invest his £1500 savings. How much money will he have after 4 years if he puts it in a savings account that pays a) 8% compound interest per year,
b) 10% simple interest per year?

12) What is The Golden Rule for finding the 'Best Buy'?

13) Charley loves ham. Two different sized tins of Froggatt's Ham are on sale in his local shop. Which one is the 'Best Buy' for Charley?

14) A TV is on sale for £1500. It can be bought on hire purchase for a 20% deposit followed by 24 monthly payments of £60. What is the hire purchase price?

15) Laura is planning a walk in the countryside. The route she has planned is 15 km long. Laura knows that she walks at an average speed of 4 km/h. It gets dark at 5 pm. What is the latest time Laura should set off walking in order to get back before dark?

Metric and Imperial Units

This topic is easy marks — make sure you get them. That sounded a bit like a threat. It wasn't. Honest. I just have poor people skills.

Metric Units

1) Length mm, cm, m, km
2) Area mm^2, cm^2, m^2, km^2,
3) Volume mm^3, cm^3, m^3, litres, ml
4) Weight g, kg, tonnes
5) Speed km/h, m/s

MEMORISE THESE KEY FACTS:

1cm = 10mm	1 tonne = 1000kg
1m = 100cm	1 litre = 1000ml
1km = 1000m	1 litre = 1000 cm^3
1kg = 1000g	1 cm^3 = 1 ml

Imperial Units

1) Length Inches, feet, yards, miles
2) Area Square inches, square feet, square yards, square miles
3) Volume Cubic inches, cubic feet, gallons, pints
4) Weight ounces, pounds, stones, tons
5) Speed mph

1 Foot = 12 Inches
1 Yard = 3 Feet
1 Gallon = 8 Pints
1 Stone = 14 Pounds (lbs)
1 Pound = 16 Ounces (oz)

Metric-Imperial Conversions

You could get asked to convert between metric and imperial units in the exam. Approximate conversions are used to calculate how many metric units make up an imperial unit, and vice versa.

Approximate Conversions

1 gallon = 4.5 litres	1 m = 1.1 yards
1 foot = 30 cm	1 inch = 2.5 cm
1 metric tonne = 1 imperial ton	

YOU NEED TO LEARN THESE THREE CONVERSIONS — they DON'T promise to give you them in the Exam and if they're feeling mean (as they often are), they won't.

1 kg = 2.2 lbs
1 litre = 1 ¾ Pints
1 mile = 1.6 km or 5 miles = 8 km

Imperial units — they're mint...

Learn the conversions above, then cover the page and see if you can scribble them all down.

1) a) How many cm is 2 metres? b) How many mm is 6.5cm?
2) a) How many kg is 2500g? b) How many litres is 1500 cm^3?
3) A rod is 46 inches long. What is this in feet and inches?
4) a) Roughly how many yards is 200m? b) How many cm is 6 feet 3 inches?

Conversion Factors

Conversion Factors are a really good way of dealing with all sorts of questions and the method is dead easy. Prepare yourself for the 3 steps towards conversion-related happiness...

Method

1) Find the CONVERSION FACTOR (always easy).
2) Multiply AND divide by it.
3) Choose the COMMON SENSE ANSWER.

Example 1:

"A Giant Sea-slug called Kevin was washed up near Grange-Over-Sands. He was 18.6 m in length. How long is this in yards?"

Check page 21 for the conversion factors.

Step 1) Find the CONVERSION FACTOR
In this question the Conversion Factor = 1.1
— because 1 m = 1.1 yards

Step 2) MULTIPLY AND DIVIDE by the conversion factor:
18.6 m × 1.1 = 20.5 yards
18.6 m ÷ 1.1 = 16.9 yards

Step 3) Choose the COMMON SENSE answer:
The answer is that 18.6 m = 20.5 yards (yards are shorter than metres so the number of yards will be bigger than the number of metres)

Example 2:

"If £1 is equal to 1.7 US Dollars, how much is 63 US Dollars in £s?"

Step 1) Find the CONVERSION FACTOR
In this question the Conversion Factor is obviously 1.7
(When you're changing foreign money it's called the 'Exchange Rate')

Step 2) MULTIPLY AND DIVIDE by the conversion factor:
63 × 1.7 = 107.1 = £107.10
63 ÷ 1.7 = 37.06 = £37.06

Step 3) Choose the COMMON SENSE answer:
Since 1.7 US Dollars = £1, you're clearly going to have fewer pounds than you had Dollars (roughly half). In other words, the answer has to be less than 63, so it's £37.06

Measuring

You've probably got lots of scales lying around at home. A scale is just something with lots of lines and numbers that you use to measure things — like rulers, measuring jugs and thermometers.

Reading scales is pretty simple — just follow these steps:

1) If the thing you're measuring lines up with a number on the scale, then just read off the number.
2) Otherwise you'll have to work out how big the divisions of the scale are, and count the number of divisions.
3) When you give your answer, always say whether it's in metres or centimetres or whatever.

EXAMPLES:

The bulldog is 70 cm tall

The cylinder contains 4.2 ml of slug juice

Measurements Need to be Rounded Off

Take this slimy grey slug for example (a much smaller relative of Kevin from p22):

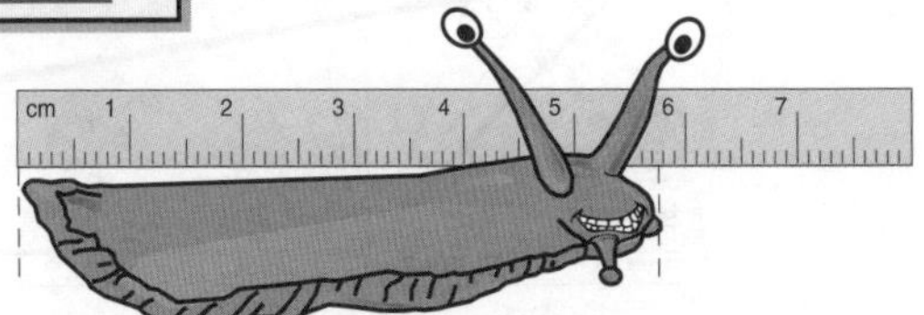

It has a length somewhere between 5 cm and 6 cm and if you look closer you can even say it's somewhere between 5.7 cm and 5.8 cm, but you can't really tell any more accurately than that.

So really we only know its length to within 0.1 cm.

The thing is though that whenever you measure such things as lengths, weights, speeds etc, you always have to take your answer to a certain level of accuracy because you can never get the exact answer.

The simple rule is: **You always round off to the number that it's NEAREST TO**

If we take our slimy slug, then to the nearest cm his length is 6 cm (rather than 5 cm) and to the nearest 0.1 cm it's 5.8 cm (rather than 5.7)

There is Always an Error in Measurement

Rounding means that there is always an ERROR IN MEASUREMENT:

The simple rule is this: **The real value can be as much as HALF THE ROUNDED UNIT above and below the rounded-off value.**

E.g. If a length is given as 2.4 m to the nearest 0.1 m, the real value could be 2.4 m ± 0.05 m.
So the answer could be anything between 2.35 m (the lower bound) and 2.45 m (the upper bound).

Should be room for the gag on this page — nope... I've made an error in measurement

Plenty of stuff to remember on this page next time you go out slug measuring...
Remember to note the value of divisions when reading scales and don't forget errors in measurement.

Measuring and Drawing Angles

Need to measure an angle? DON'T PANIC, just reach for your protractor and follow this advice...

Using Protractors

The 2 big mistakes that people make with PROTRACTORS:

1) Not putting the 0° line at the start position
2) Reading from the WRONG SCALE.

These scales won't work.

Two Rules for Getting it Right

1) ALWAYS position the protractor with the bottom edge of it along one of the lines as shown here:

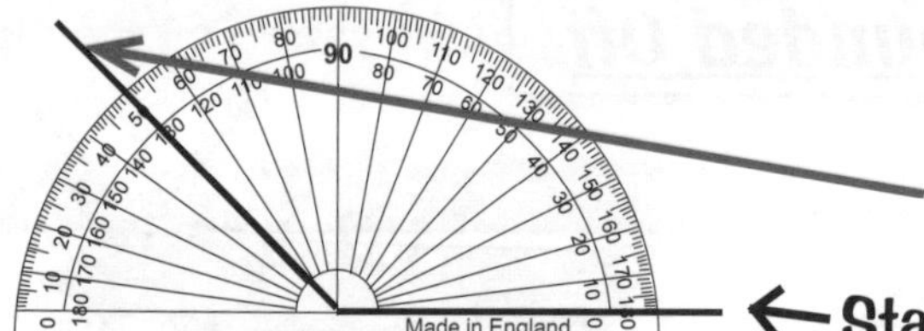

2) COUNT THE ANGLE IN 10° STEPS from the start line right round to the other one.

DON'T JUST READ A NUMBER OFF THE SCALE — chances are it'll be the WRONG ONE because there are TWO scales to choose from.

The answer here is 130° — NOT 50° — which you will only get right if you start counting 10°, 20°, 30°, 40° etc. from the start line until you reach the other line. You should also estimate it as a check.

Neither will these.

Drawing Angles

EXAMPLE: Draw a 70° angle.

1) Draw a dot.
2) Place the centre of your protractor over the dot.
3) Put one dot at the 0° marker.
4) Follow the scale from 0° up to your angle and put another dot.
5) Join the centre dot to each of the other dots.

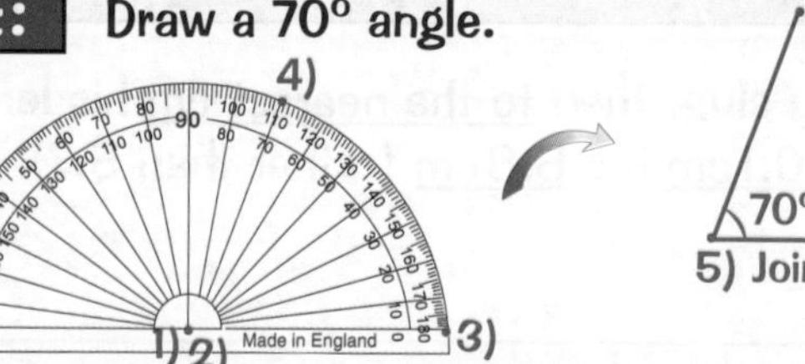

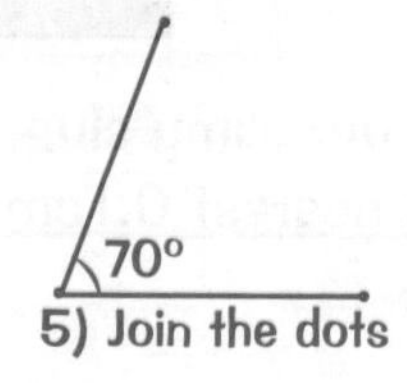

If you're drawing an angle between 180° to 360°:

1) Subtract your angle from 360.
2) Draw the resulting angle (use the normal method)
3) Draw the angle marker on, the wrong way round.

330°

My dad's pretty decent at farming — he drives a pro-tractor...

Ho, ho, ho — pretty funny aren't I. Anyway, moving on...

1) LEARN 2 rules for using protractors.
2) Use a protractor to accurately draw these angles: a) 35° b) 330° c) 80°

Maps and Scale Drawings

If maps were the same size as the place they were showing, then they'd be big... and a bit pointless. Thankfully maps are usually made using scales. The most usual map scale is '1 cm = so many km'. This just tells you how many km in real life it is for 1 cm measured on the actual map itself.

1) Converting 'cm on the Map' into 'Real km'

This map shows the original Roman M6 Motorway built by the Emperor Hadrian in the year AD120.

The scale of the map is '1cm to 8km'
"Work out the length of the section of M6 between Wigan and Preston."

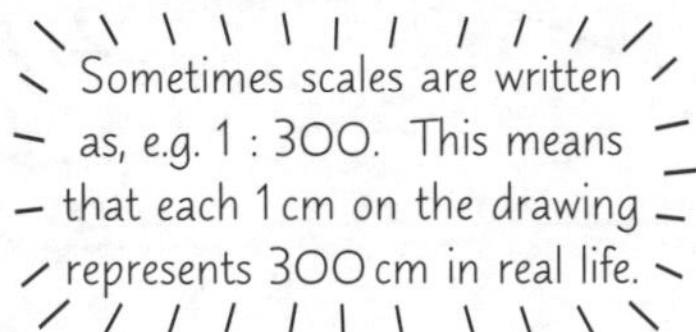

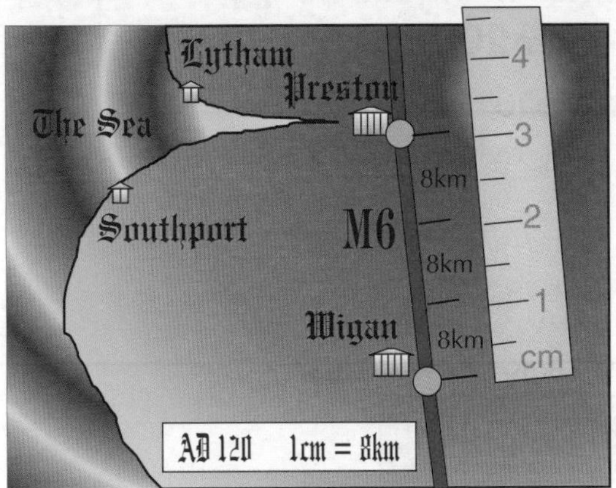

This is what you do (as shown on the diagram)

1) PUT YOUR RULER AGAINST THE THING you're finding the length of
2) MARK OFF EACH WHOLE CM AND WRITE IN THE DISTANCE IN KM next to each one.
3) ADD UP ALL THE KM DISTANCES TO FIND THE WHOLE LENGTH of the road in km. (i.e. 8 km + 8 km + 8 km = 24 km)

2) Converting 'Real km' into 'cm on the Map'

Example:

"A map is drawn on a scale of 1 cm to 2 km. If a road is 12 km long in real life, how long will it be in cm on the map?"

Answer:

1) Start by drawing the road as a straight line:

2) Mark off each cm and fill in how many km it is for each one

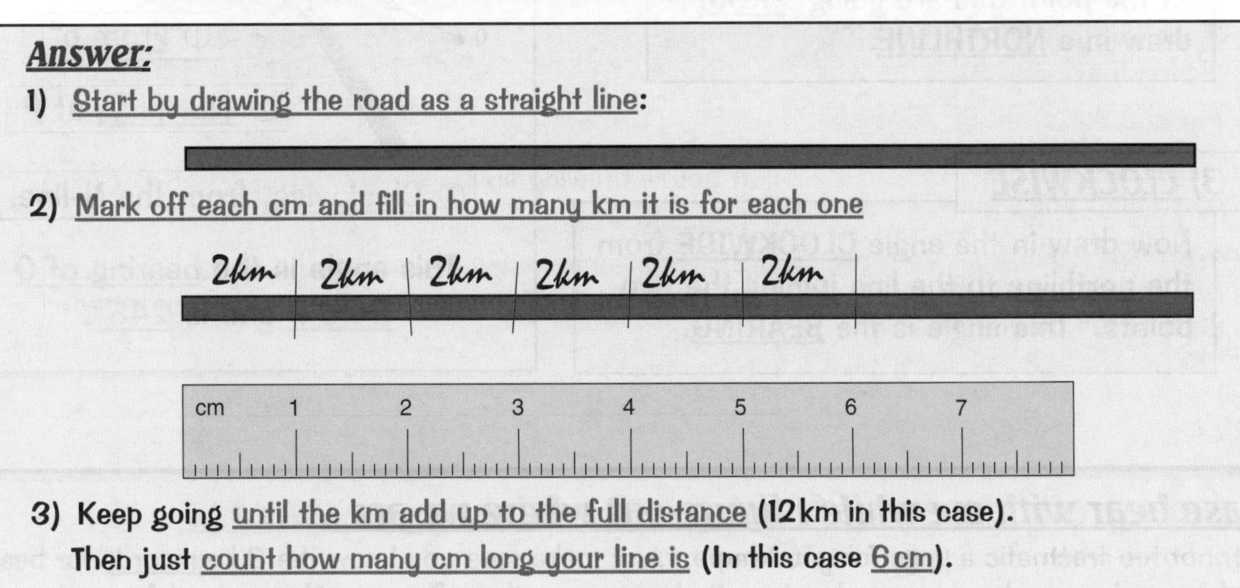

3) Keep going until the km add up to the full distance (12 km in this case). Then just count how many cm long your line is (In this case 6 cm).

Bearings

By the end of this page you should have got your bearings about what is meant by bearings. Ahem.

Bearings

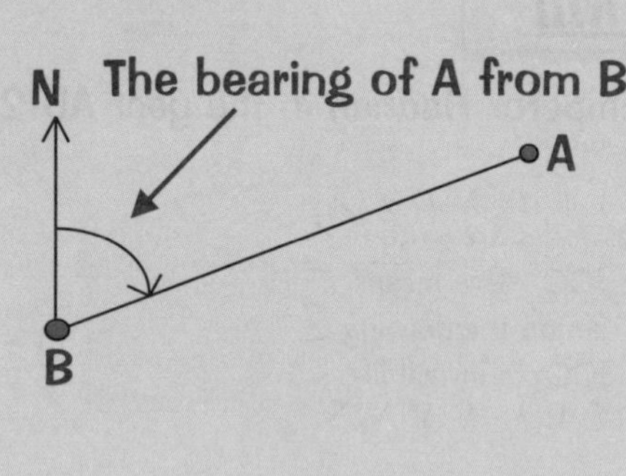

1) A bearing is just a DIRECTION given as an ANGLE in degrees.
2) All bearings are measured CLOCKWISE from the NORTHLINE.
3) All bearings are given as 3 figures: e.g. 060° rather than just 60°, 020° rather than 20° etc.

The 3 Key Words

Only learn this if you want to get bearings RIGHT

1) 'FROM'

Find the word 'FROM' in the question, and put your pencil on the diagram at the point you are going 'from'.

2) NORTHLINE

At the point you are going 'FROM', draw in a NORTHLINE.

3) CLOCKWISE

Now draw in the angle CLOCKWISE from the northline to the line joining the two points. This angle is the BEARING.

EXAMPLE:

Find the bearing of Q from P:

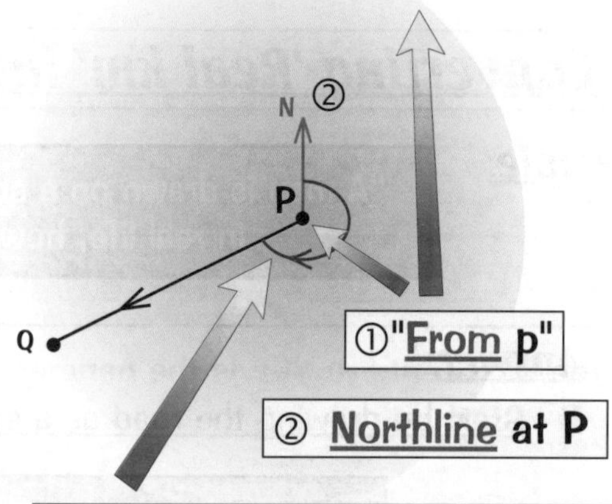

This angle is the bearing of Q from P and is 245°.

Please bear with me while I figure out where we are...

Right, not too traumatic a page for you I hope. Just make sure you know the 3 key words for bearings. And always, always, always remember to write bearings as three figures. Always (and forever).

1) Draw a blob on a piece of paper to represent home, and a line going out on a bearing of 080°.

Perimeters

Perimeter is the distance all the way around the outside of a 2D shape. It's pretty straightforward to work out if you use the big blob method. So pay attention — this could be easy marks.

The Perimeter is the Distance Around the Edge of a Shape

To find a PERIMETER, you ADD UP THE LENGTHS OF ALL THE SIDES, but...
THE ONLY RELIABLE WAY to make sure you get all the sides is this:

1) PUT A BIG BLOB AT ONE CORNER and then go around the shape.
2) WRITE DOWN THE LENGTH OF EVERY SIDE as you go along.
3) EVEN SIDES THAT SEEM TO HAVE NO LENGTH GIVEN — you must work them out.
4) Keep going until you get back to the BIG BLOB.

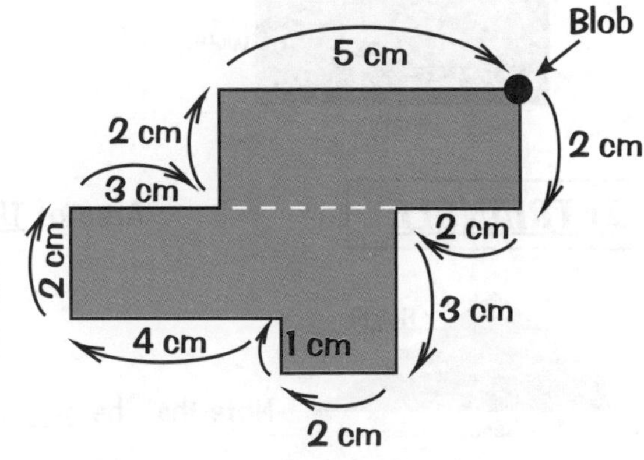

E.g. $2+2+3+2+1+4+2+3+2+5 = \underline{26\text{ cm}}$

Yes, I know you think it's yet another fussy method, but believe me, it's so easy to miss a side. You must use good reliable methods for everything — or you'll lose marks willy nilly.

Finding the perimeter of a regular shape (a shape where all the sides are the same length and all the angles are the same) is dead easy — you just find the length of one side and multiply it by the number of sides.

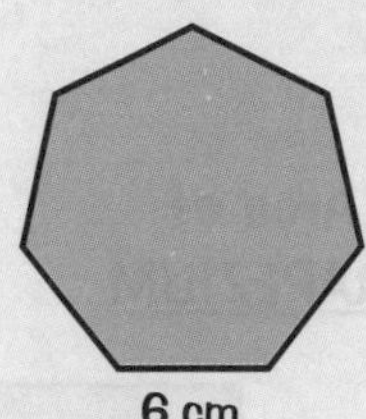

E.g. for this lovely heptagon, each side is 6 cm long. There are 7 sides, so Perimeter = $6 \times 7 = \underline{42\text{ cm}}$.

Perimeters of Circles and Semicircles

1) The CIRCUMFERENCE is the perimeter of a circle.

CIRCUMFERENCE = $\pi \times$ Diameter

$$C = \pi \times D$$

$\pi = 3.141592....$
$= \underline{3.14}$ (approx)

2) The perimeter of a SEMICIRCLE, is half of the circumference of the circle, plus the diameter:

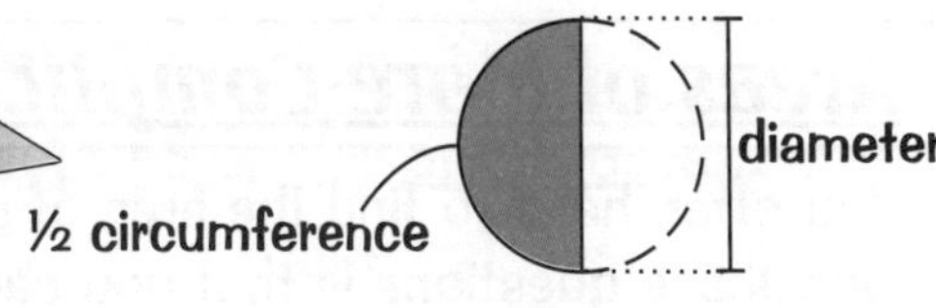

Perimeter of semicircle = diameter + $\frac{1}{2}$ × circumference

RUN — DON'T WALK from... the BIG BLOB...

...no, don't do that really. You need to get friendly with your big blob, and always use him for finding the perimeter of complicated shapes.

1) Turn over and write down what you have learnt.
2) Find the perimeter of the shape shown here.

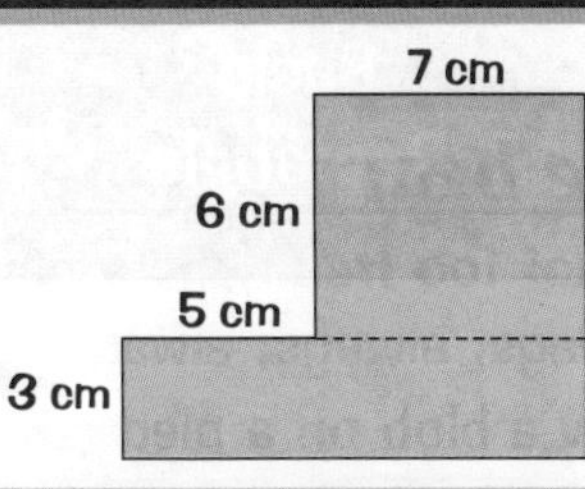

Areas

First things first — below are five basic area formulas. Best learn these unless you're planning on tipping bucketloads of easy exam marks down the toilet.

You must LEARN these Formulas:

1) RECTANGLE

Area of RECTANGLE = length × width

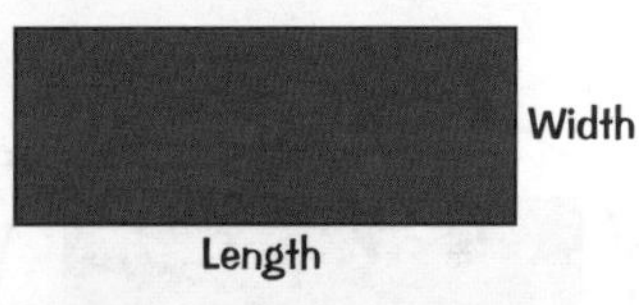

$$A = l \times w$$

2) TRIANGLE

Area of TRIANGLE = ½ × base × vertical height

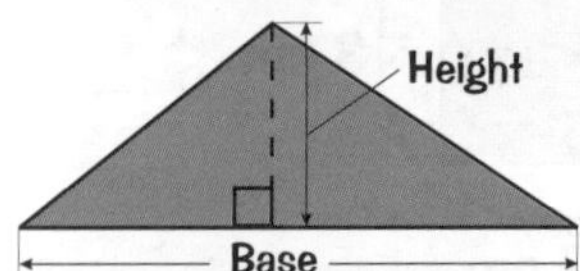

$$A = \tfrac{1}{2} \times b \times h_v$$

Note that the height must always be the vertical height, not the sloping height.

3) PARALLELOGRAM

Area of PARALLELOGRAM = base × vertical height

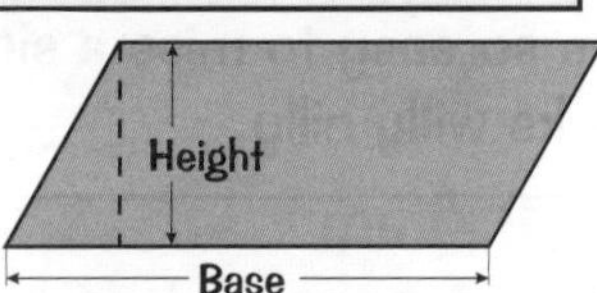

$$A = b \times h_v$$

4) TRAPEZIUM

Area of TRAPEZIUM = average of parallel sides × distance between them

a, h, b

$$A = \tfrac{1}{2} \times (a + b) \times h$$

5) CIRCLE

Area of CIRCLE = π × (radius)²

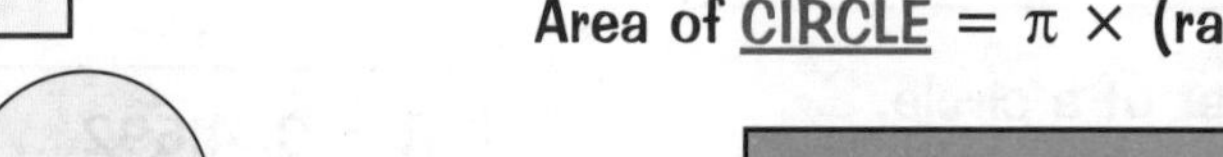

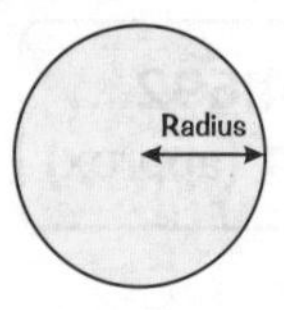

$$A = \pi \times r^2$$

To work out the area of a semicircle use the same formula and then divide by 2.

Areas of More Complicated Shapes

You often have to find the area of strange looking shapes in exam questions. What you always find with these questions is that you can break the shape up into simpler ones that you can deal with.

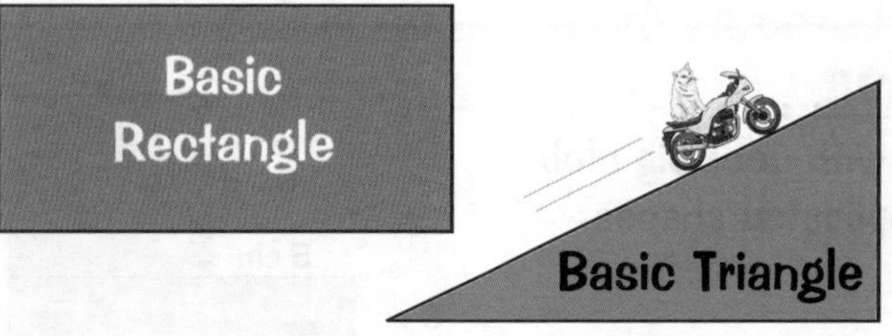

1) SPLIT THEM UP into the two basic shapes: RECTANGLE and TRIANGLE
2) Work out the area of each bit SEPARATELY
3) Then ADD THEM ALL TOGETHER

See next page for a lovely example...

Areas

...and here's the lovely example, as promised...

EXAMPLE: Work out the area of the shape shown:

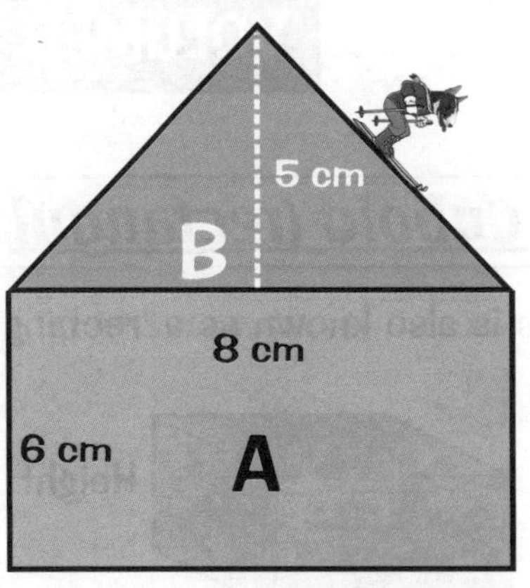

ANSWER:

Shape A is a rectangle:

Area = L × W
= 8 × 6
= 48 cm²

Shape B is a triangle:

Area = ½ × b × h
= ½ × 8 × 5
= 20 cm²

TOTAL AREA = 48 + 20 = 68 cm²

Don't Reach Straight for the Calculator

Exam marks you say? I might be able to get my hands on some. Meet me by the sewers at sunset. Come alone.

You might be kidding yourself that it 'takes too long' to write down your working out — but what's so great about getting ZERO MARKS for an easy question?

Compare these two answers for finding the area of the triangle opposite:

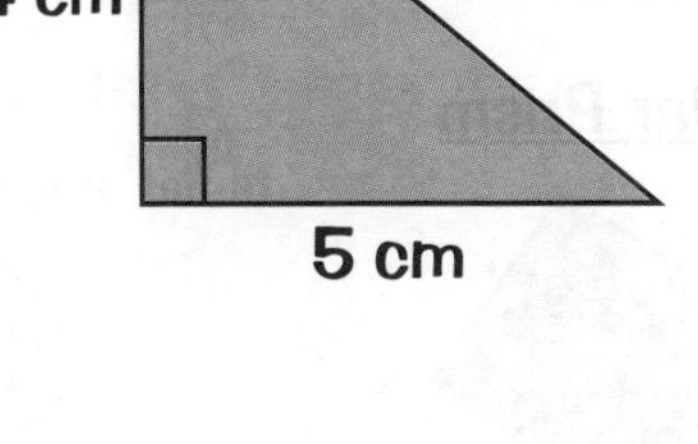

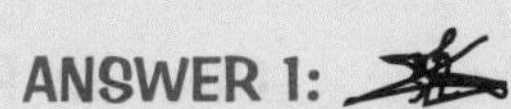

ANSWER 1 gets NO MARKS AT ALL — 20 is the wrong answer and there's nothing else to give any marks for.

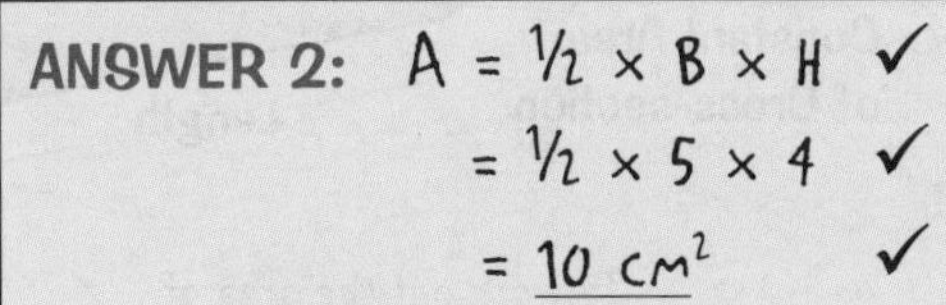

ANSWER 2 has 3 bits that all get marks, — so even if the answer was wrong it would still get most of the marks!

The thing is though, when you write it down step by step, you can see what you're doing and you won't get it wrong in the first place — try it next time, go on... just for the wild experience.

I need to take my shape to the barbers — it's getting area and area...

Hahaha.... Not amused? OK suit yourself. It's time to memorise the area formulas and learn how to deal with complicated shapes. Then find the areas of these 4 shapes...

1)

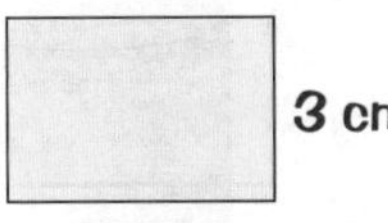

2)

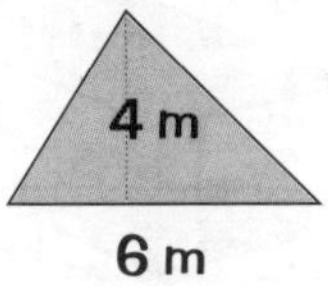

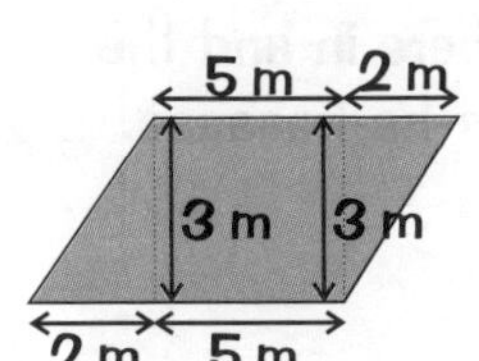

3)

4)

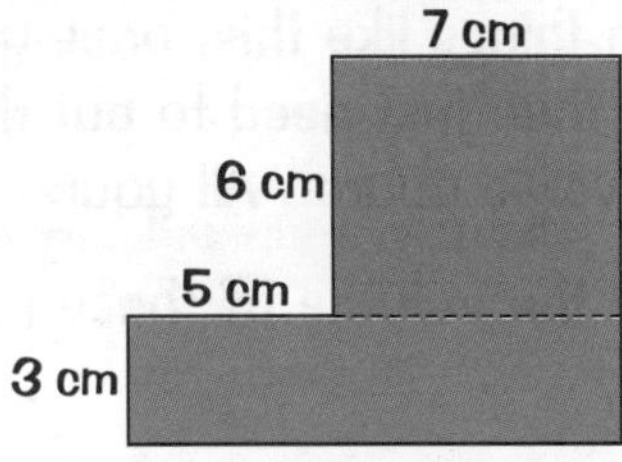

Volume

I'm not going to say anything apart from...

VOLUMES — YOU MUST LEARN THESE TOO

1) Cuboid (rectangular block)

(This is also known as a 'rectangular prism' — see below to understand why.)

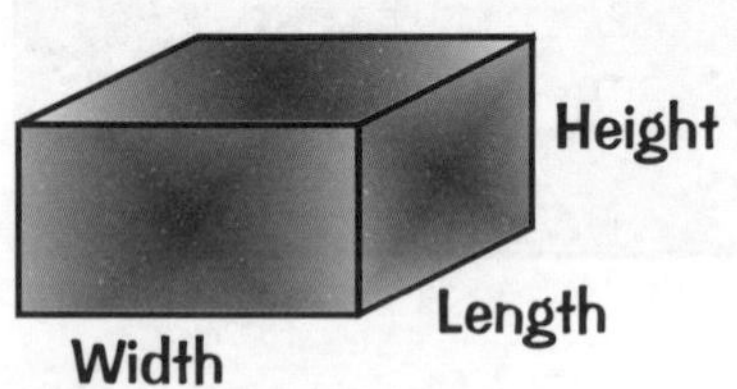

Volume of Cuboid = length × width × height

(The other word for volume is CAPACITY)

2) Prism

A PRISM is a solid (3-D) object which is the same shape all the way through — i.e. it has a CONSTANT AREA OF CROSS-SECTION.

Now, for some reason, not a lot of people know what a prism is, but they come up all the time in Exams, so make sure YOU know.

Triangular Prism

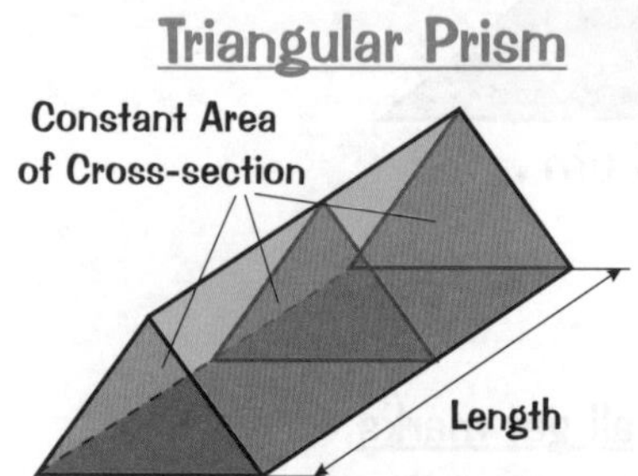

Hexagonal Prism
(a flat one, certainly, but still a prism)

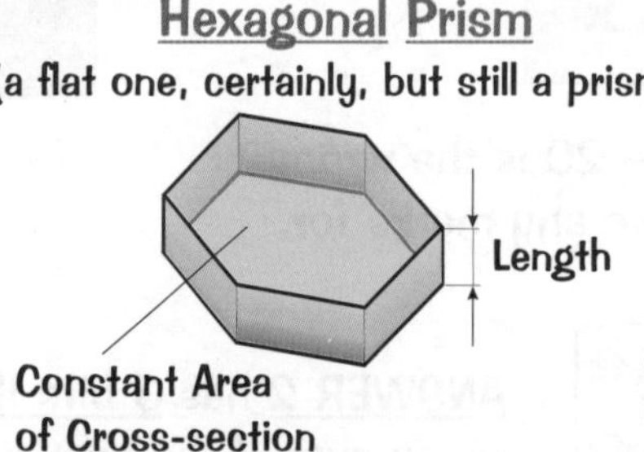

Circular Prism
(or Cylinder)

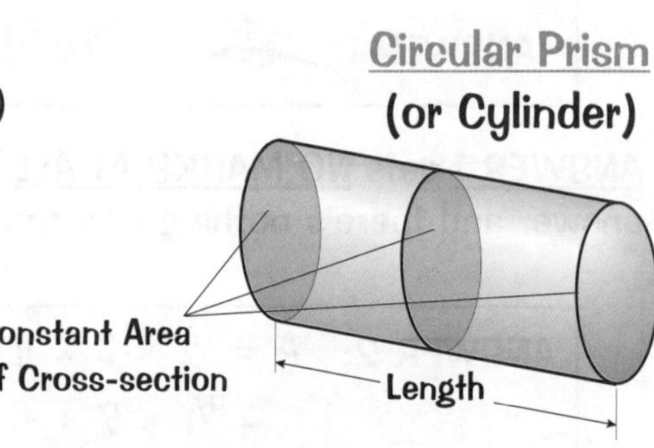

Volume of prism = Cross-sectional Area × length

$V = A \times l$

As you can see, the formula for the volume of a prism is very simple. The difficult part, usually, is finding the area of the cross-section.

Don't make it any more angry — it's already a cross-section...

With things like this, once you've learnt the formula it's a doddle. You then just need to put the right numbers in and the answer is yours. All yours. Mwah-ha-ha-ha-haaaaaa.

Find the volume of these prisms:

a)

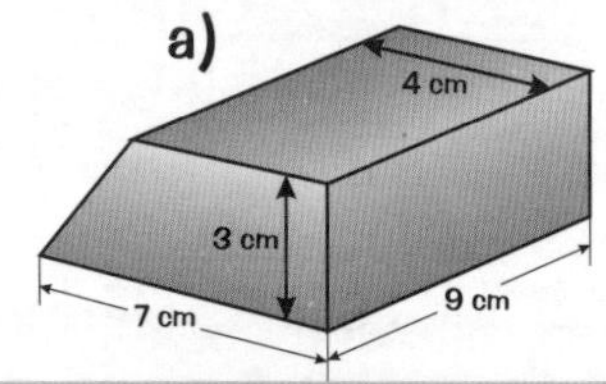

b)

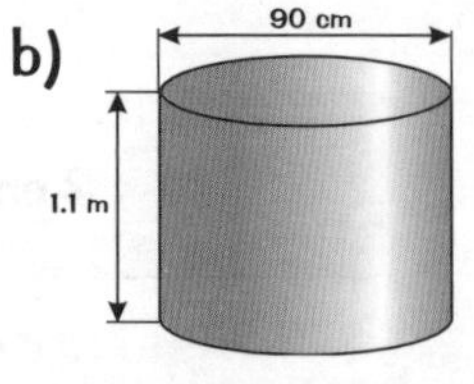

Clock Time Questions

You see 24 hour clocks in lots of places so hopefully you're an expert in how to read them. The only thing you might need reminding about is 'am' and 'pm' in the 12 hour clock:

20:23:47

08:23:47

1) am and pm

'am' means 'morning'. It runs from 12 midnight to 12 noon.
'pm' means 'afternoon and evening'. It runs from 12 noon to 12 midnight.

(though I guess you know that already)

2) Conversions

You'll definitely need to know these very important facts:

1 day = 24 hours
1 hour = 60 minutes
1 minute = 60 seconds

3) Exam questions involving 'time'

There are lots of different questions they can ask involving time but the same GOOD OLD RELIABLE DEPENDABLE METHOD will work wonders on all of them.
"And what is this good old reliable dependable method?", I hear you cry. Well, it's this:

Take your time, write it down, and split it up into SHORT EASY STAGES

EXAMPLE: Find the time taken by a train which sets off at 13:25 and arrives at 19:10.

WHAT YOU DON'T DO is try to work it all out in your head in one go — this method fails nearly every time. Instead, split it into short easy stages like this:

13:25 → (35 mins) 14:00 → (5 hours) 19:00 → (10 mins) 19:10

This is a nice safe way of finding the total time from 13:25 to 19:10.
5 hours + 35 mins + 10 mins = 5 hours 45 mins.

4) If you use your Calculator, beware...

Try to avoid using the calculator with time measurements — it's a pain in the neck. You'll get answers in decimals, and you have to convert them into hours and minutes. So learn this example:

2.5 hours = 2 ½ hours = 2 hours and 30 minutes

That sound right? Of course it does.

SO DON'T GO WRITING ANYTHING STUPID, like: **2.5 hours = 2 hours and 50 minutes** ← WRONG WRONG WRONG WRONG!!

BREAKING NEWS: Public panic after warning over calculator use...

You probably know lots of this stuff already. The tips are useful though — so don't just ignore them.

1) What is 17:15 in 12 hour clock? (don't forget am/pm)
2) A plane sets off at 10:15 am. The flight lasts 5 hrs 50 mins. What is the arrival time?
3) How many minutes are there in a day? And how many seconds are there in a day?
4) What is 3.5 hours in hours and minutes? What is 5¾ hours in hours and minutes?

Collecting Data

Statistics is a type of maths that involves investigations, gathering data and analysing results. The first step in many investigations is coming up with a hypothesis...

A Hypothesis is a Statement you can Test

A HYPOTHESIS is a statement that you think is true but you haven't got evidence to support yet. A hypothesis must be testable.

EXAMPLE:

Imagine you're investigating whether temperature affects how many people go to the beach. The first thing you need to do is come up with a hypothesis that you can test:

1) First, decide what you expect the effect will be.

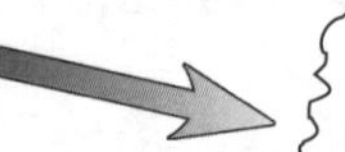

I reckon more people go to the beach when it's warmer.

2) Then turn it into a testable statement:

The higher the temperature, the more people go to the beach.

This is your hypothesis.

3) Once you have a hypothesis you can start to collect data.

Questionnaires Can be Used to Collect Data

Questionnaires are a common way of collecting data, which means they're a favourite with examiners. You might be asked to comment on how good a question is, or write some questions of your own. Either way, you need to bear these points in mind:

1) QUESTIONS MUST BE RELEVANT — they should give you evidence for or against your hypothesis. It's no use asking fascinating questions if the answers aren't useful. E.g. the question: 'What do you like best about beaches?' isn't relevant to the hypothesis above.
2) THEY SHOULD BE EASY TO UNDERSTAND — if people don't understand them they're no good. E.g. 'How do you feel about the temperature at the beach?' is difficult to answer as it's not clear exactly what the question means.
3) ALLOW FOR ALL POSSIBLE ANSWERS TO YOUR QUESTION — e.g. 'What is your favourite subject: Maths, English or Science?' is difficult to answer truthfully if you like Art best. A better question would be 'What is your favourite subject?'.
4) QUESTIONS SHOULDN'T BE LEADING — leading questions suggest what answer is wanted. E.g. 'You do agree that thrash metal is really good music?'. The problem with this question is that it could make the interviewee feel pressurised into saying 'yes'. A better question would be "What type of music do you prefer to listen to?"
5) REMEMBER PEOPLE MAY NOT ANSWER QUESTIONS TRUTHFULLY — e.g. 'What is your age?' might be a sensitive question for some people. It can help to provide age categories, e.g. 'over 50' so they don't have to answer with their exact age.

Hypothesis — the more revision you do the better your exam grade will be

Sadly, a questionnaire won't help you to test this hypothesis. The only way to find out for sure is to revise loads, sit the exam, then sit back and wait for the super duper grades to come rolling in. Great.

Frequency Tables

Frequency tables can either be done in rows or in columns of numbers. They can be quite confusing, but they're not too bad if you learn these key points:

1) The word FREQUENCY just means HOW MANY, so a frequency table is nothing more than a 'How many in each group' table.
2) The FIRST ROW (or column) just gives the GROUP LABELS.
3) The SECOND ROW (or column) gives the ACTUAL DATA.

Frequency Tables Can be Drawn in Row or Column Form

Here is a typical frequency table in ROW FORM and COLUMN FORM:

Row Form

No. of Sisters	0	1	2	3	4	5	6
Frequency	7	15	12	8	3	1	0

Column Form

No. of Sisters	Frequency
0	7
1	15
2	12
3	8
4	3
5	1
6	0
Totals	46

You May Have to Draw a Frequency Table From Data

EXAMPLE A hockey team lists the number of goals they score in each match of a season. Draw a frequency table for the data. 1, 2, 0, 3, 2, 1, 0, 2, 3, 2, 2, 1, 2, 0, 1, 5

Start by drawing a table with 3 columns — label them "no. of goals", "tally" and "frequency". Then follow these steps:

1) Fill in the group labels — here it's numbers of goals. You need to cover the whole range (0 – 5).

No. of Goals	Tally	Frequency
0					3
1						4
2	~~				~~		6
3				2
4		0
5			1

2) Draw a tally mark to represent the number of goals in each match. Tallies are bunched together in fives, e.g. ~~||||~~ = 5.

3) Add up the tally marks in each row to find the frequency.

It's a good idea to cross off your data as you go, e.g. ~~1~~, ~~2~~, ~~0~~, 3... so you don't miss one or count one twice.

My table has 5 columns, 6 rows and 4 legs...

Learn the rules for frequency tables, then turn over and write them down to see what you know. The best way of getting your head round this is to practise doing it, so have a go yourself. You could ask your class how many times they've been to Bury. Then put the results in a frequency table.

Grouped Frequency Tables

Frequency tables often group data together to make it easier to understand. I, on the other hand, like to write with my eyes closed to make it harder to understand. But that's just me.

Example 1:

The marks of 28 students in a test (out of 80) were:

63, 45, 44, 52, 58,
49, 48, 22, 37, 34,
44, 49, 66, 73, 69,
32, 49, 29, 55, 57,
30, 72, 59, 46, 70,
39, 27, 40

As a Grouped Table

Marks	Tally	Frequency
$0 \leq x \leq 10$		
$11 \leq x \leq 20$		
$21 \leq x \leq 30$	IIII	4
$31 \leq x \leq 40$	~~IIII~~	5
$41 \leq x \leq 50$	~~IIII~~ III	8
$51 \leq x \leq 60$	~~IIII~~	5
$61 \leq x \leq 70$	IIII	4
$71 \leq x \leq 80$	II	2
		28

Example 2:

The weights (in kg) of a bunch of 20 school kids are shown below.

67.3, 45.6, 47.7, 65.0, 54.2,
76.5, 44.6, 34.3, 69.8, 53.9,
32.3, 54.5, 78.9, 59.8, 57.4,
30.0, 79.1, 46.2, 66.0, 51.6

As a Grouped Table

Weight w (kg)	Tally	Frequency
$30 \leq w < 40$	III	3
$40 \leq w < 50$	IIII	4
$50 \leq w < 60$	~~IIII~~ I	6
$60 \leq w < 70$	IIII	4
$70 \leq w < 80$	III	3
		20

Reading the Intervals

In the top table, '$0 \leq x \leq 10$' means x is either between 0 and 10 or it is one of those values.

In the bottom table, '$30 \leq w < 40$' means w is between 30 and 40 or it could equal 30, but it can't equal 40 (40 would go in the next group).

The intervals used in the top table are suitable for whole number data (note that you couldn't place 30.5 on this table — it would fall in between two groups). Whole numbers are an example of discrete data — data that can only take certain values.

The intervals in the bottom table are suitable for any numbers (30.5, 50.9999) because there are no gaps between the groups. Data like this that can take any values within a range is called continuous data.

Discretion is the better part of valour...

Learn the difference between discrete and continuous data — you'll lose marks if you get them mixed up. Think of your own examples for each type — e.g. the number of celebrities I stalk each day is discrete data, and the length of time it takes the police to arrive to arrest me is continuous. On a slightly less creepy note... 1) Say if the following are continuous or discrete data and design a data table for each one: a) shoe size of 20 adults b) height of 30 adults.

Mean, Median, Mode and Range

If you don't manage to learn the 4 basic definitions then you'll be passing up on some of the easiest marks in the whole Exam. It can't be that difficult can it?

1) MODE = MOST common

Mode = most (emphasise the 'o' in each when you say them)

2) MEDIAN = MIDDLE value

Median = mid (emphasise the m*d in each when you say them)

3) MEAN = TOTAL of items ÷ NUMBER of items

Mean is just the average, 'but it's mean 'cos you have to work it out'

4) RANGE = How far from the smallest to the biggest

THE GOLDEN RULE:

Mean, median, mode and range should be easy marks but even people who've gone to the incredible extent of learning them still manage to lose marks in the Exam because they don't do this one vital step:

Always REARRANGE the data in ASCENDING ORDER

(and then check you have the same number of entries)

Example:

"Find the mean, median, mode and range of these numbers:"

2, 5, 3, 2, 6, -4, 0, 9, -3, 1, 6, 3, -2, 3 (14)

1) FIRST... rearrange them: -4, -3, -2, 0, 1, 2, 2, 3, 3, 3, 5, 6, 6, 9 (✓14)

2) MEAN $= \frac{\text{total}}{\text{number}} = \frac{-4-3-2+0+1+2+2+3+3+3+5+6+6+9}{14}$

$= 31 \div 14 = \underline{2.21}$

3) MEDIAN = the middle value (only when they're arranged in order of size, that is).

When there are two middle numbers, as in this case, then the median is halfway between the two middle numbers.

-4, -3, -2, 0, 1, 2, 2, 3, 3, 3, 5, 6, 6, 9

← seven numbers this side seven numbers this side →

Median = 2.5

4) MODE = most common value, which is simply 3. (Or you can say "The modal value is 3")

5) RANGE = distance from lowest to highest value, i.e. from -4 up to 9, = 13

Don't forget the order — socks and then shoes...

Trust me — it's easily done. Learn the four definitions and the Golden Rule, then cover this page and write them all down from memory. Then be a clever bunny and use everything you've learnt to find the mean, median, mode and range for this set of data: 1, 3, 14, -5, 6, -12, 18, 7, 23, 10, -5, -14, 0, 25, 8

Mean, Median, Mode and Range

Get the book at a good range from your eyes and then switch to reading mode...

Finding the Mean, Mode and Median From Frequency Tables

Example:

No. of Sisters	0	1	2	3	4	5	6
Frequency	7	15	12	8	3	1	0

1) The MODE is just the group with the most entries.
   In the table above the mode is 1 (sister).
2) The MEDIAN is the middle number. To find it you need to find the sum of the frequencies (7 + 15 + 12 + 8 + 3 + 1 = 46), then divide by 2. The middle number is between the 23rd and 24th values, so the median is 2 (this group contains the 22nd to the 34th values).
3) To find the MEAN for the data, you need to add an extra row:

No. of Sisters	0	1	2	3	4	5	6	Totals	
Frequency	7	15	12	8	3	1	0	46	(People asked)
No. × Frequency	0	15	24	24	12	5	0	80	(Sisters)

MEAN = 3rd Row total ÷ 2nd Row Total

Now from the table:

$$\text{MEAN} = \frac{\text{3rd row total}}{\text{2nd row total}} = \frac{80}{46} = 1.74$$ (sisters per person)

Mean sisters

Using Averages to Make Comparisons

Example — Dog Training: The dogs that were being trained were split into two teams — A and B. The table below shows the marks, out of 20, gained by the Team A dogs in an agility test.

Team A marks	3	6	6	7	9	9	10	14

1) Use the information above to calculate the mean and median marks for Team A.

   ANSWER: Mean = total of marks ÷ number of dogs = 64 ÷ 8 = 8
   Median is the middle mark. There are 8 marks so the middle is halfway between the 4th and 5th marks:

   3, 6, 6, (7, 9), 9, 10, 14 → (7 + 9) ÷ 2 = 8

2) The Team B dogs got the following results Mean = 15, Median = 16
   Which team did better? Explain your answer.

   ANSWER: You just need to compare the mean and median values for both teams.
   Your answer should go something like this...
   'Team B did better because their mean and median marks were both much higher.'

Charts and Graphs

Ooo, now it's time for a graph where you get to draw pretty pictures. And some other types, but they're not as much fun. You've still got to know them though.

1) Pictograms — these use pictures instead of numbers.

In a PICTOGRAM each picture or symbol represents a certain number of items.

EXAMPLE: The pictogram opposite shows the number of talking cats used in ridiculous TV adverts in a 3-month period:

(cat symbol) = 500 talking cats

May (3 cats) (1500 ridiculous talking cats)
June (2½ cats) (1250 ridiculous talking cats)
July (4 cats) (2000 ridiculous talking cats)

2) Bar Charts — these use bars to represent numbers.

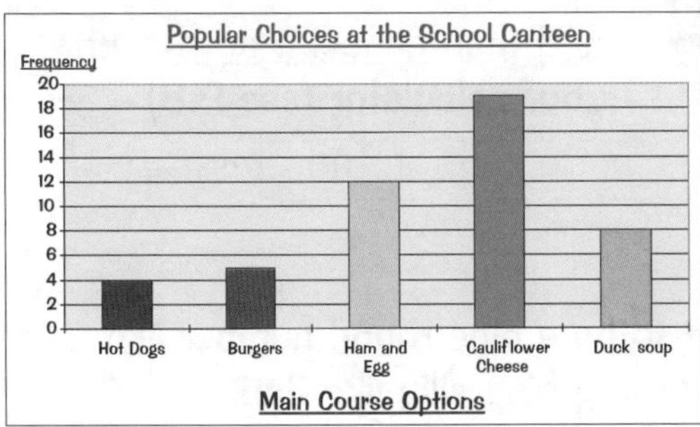

A BAR-LINE GRAPH is just like a bar chart except you draw thin lines instead of bars.

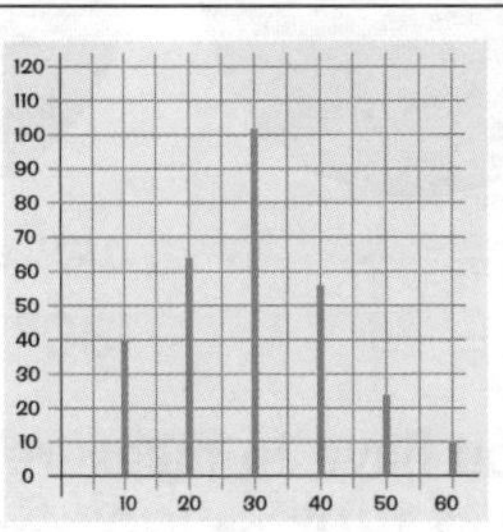

3) Two-Way Tables

Two-way tables are a bit like frequency tables, but they show two different things:

EXAMPLE:

"Use this table to work out how many
(a) right-handed people and
(b) left-handed women there were in this survey."

	Women	Men	TOTAL
Left-handed		27	63
Right-handed	164	173	
TOTAL	200	200	400

ANSWER:

(a) Either: (i) add up the number of right-handed women and the number of right-handed men. So that's 164 + 173 = 337 right-handed people.
Or: (ii) take away the total number of left-handed people from the total number of people. So that's 400 – 63 = 337 right-handed people.

	Women	Men	TOTAL
Left-handed		27	63
Right-handed	164	173	
TOTAL	200	200	400

(b) Either: (i) take away the number of right-handed women from the total number of women. That's 200 – 164 = 36 left-handed women.
Or: (ii) take away the left-handed men from the total number of left-handed people. Which would be 63 – 27 = 36 left-handed women.

	Women	Men	TOTAL
Left-handed		27	63
Right-handed	164	173	
TOTAL	200	200	400

No animals were harmed in the making of the cat pictogram above...

Ho. Ho. Have a go at sketching examples of each type of graph — just make up some data. Then copy out the two-way table, close the book and fill in the blanks. Check the numbers add up.

Charts and Graphs

In a similar way that you can make the correct combination of meat and pastry into a delicious pie, examiners can make Pie Charts into tricky exam questions. So learn the Golden Rule for Pie Charts:

The TOTAL of Everything = 360°

Remember that 360° is the trick for dealing with most Pie Charts

1) Relating Angles to Fractions

These five simplest ones you should just know straight off:

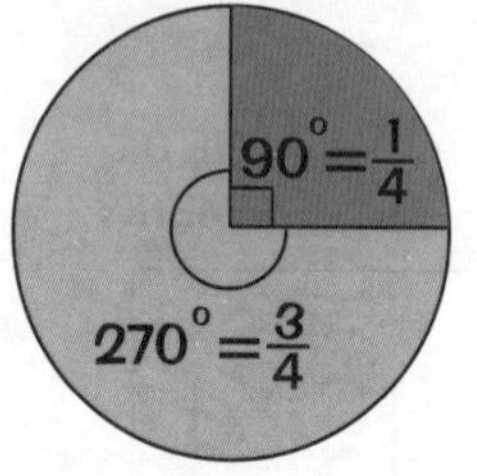

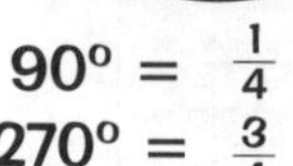

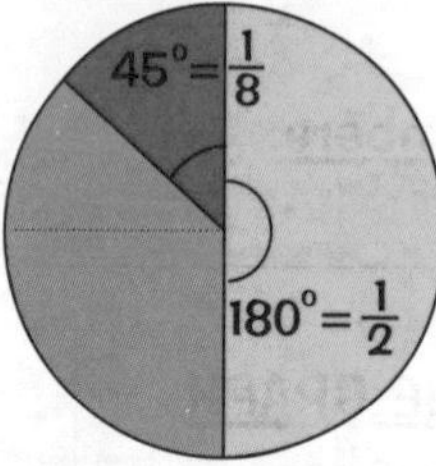

$45° = \frac{1}{8}$

$180° = \frac{1}{2}$

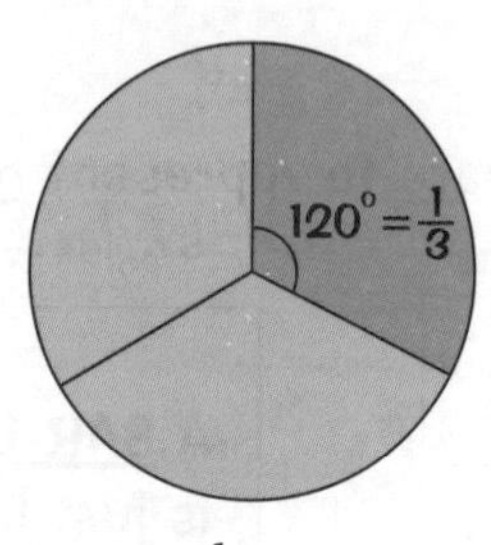

$120° = \frac{1}{3}$

For any angle the formula is:

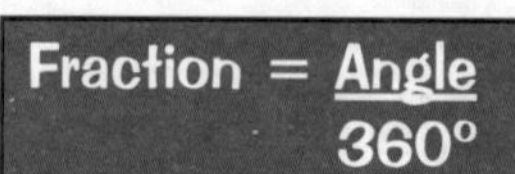

And then cancel it down with your calculator (see P.8)

If you have to measure an angle, you should expect it to be a nice round number like 90° or 180° or 120°, so don't go writing 89° or 181° or anything silly like that.

2) Relating Angles to Numbers of Other Things

Creature	Stick insects	Hamsters	Guinea pigs	Rabbits	Ducks	Total
Number	12	20	17	15	26	90
	↓	↓ ×4	↓	↓	↓	↓ ×4
Angle		80°				360°

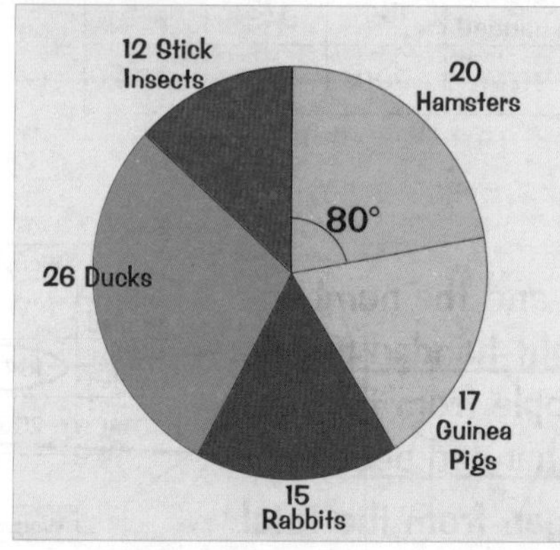

1) Add up all the numbers in each sector to get the TOTAL (90 for this one)
2) Then find the MULTIPLIER (or divider) that you need to turn your total into 360°: For 90 → 360 as above, the MULTIPLIER is 4
3) Now MULTIPLY EVERY NUMBER BY 4 to get the angle for each sector. E.g. the angle for hamsters will be

$$20 \times 4 = 80°$$

I bet you were expecting a joke about pies here...

... I'm far too witty to lower myself to making jokes about pies on a page about pie charts — that's much too obvious. There's just no need to go on and on about tasty steak-filled pies with scrumptious rich gravy on a bed of creamy mashed potato and a side order of mushy peas... mmm.

Anyway, while I'm off eating pies, you can display this data in a pie chart:

Football Team	Wigan A.	Luton	Man Utd	Others
No. of fans	53	15	30	22

Charts and Graphs

You're almost all set for the big wide world of charts and graphs — just one more page to go, and (whisper it quietly) it just so happens to be the last page of the section. HURRAH...

Line Graphs and Temperature Charts

A line graph is made up of a set of points joined with straight lines. Temperature charts are an example of a line graph — they show the variation of temperature with time.

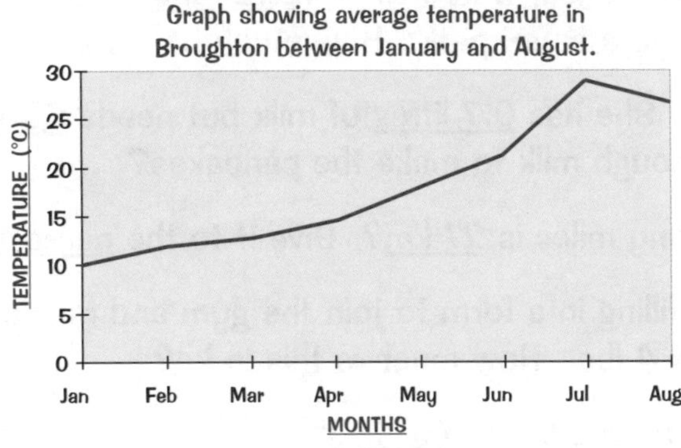

Graphs Can Sometimes be Misleading

Graphs and charts are great for displaying data, but they can be a bit confusing. So watch out...

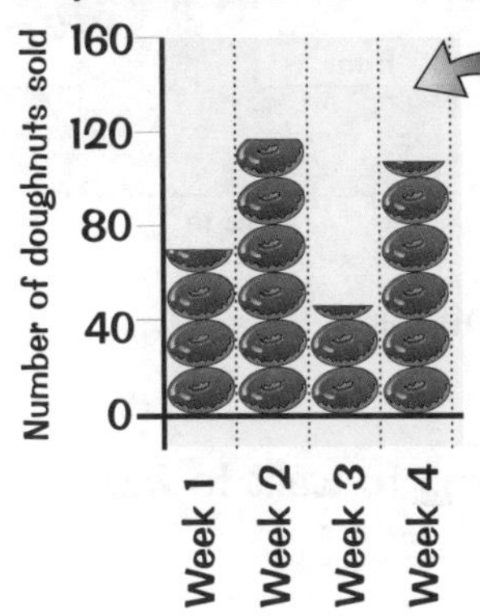

This pictogram shows the sales of doughnuts in a shop. The pictures of doughnuts show how high the bars are. They're cut to size — which is a good way of showing accurate heights.

In this pictogram some doughnuts have been SQUASHED. The heights of the bars are correct, BUT you might think the squashed doughnuts are worth the same as the 'unsquashed' doughnuts — e.g. you might think the same number of doughnuts were sold in week 4 as week 2.

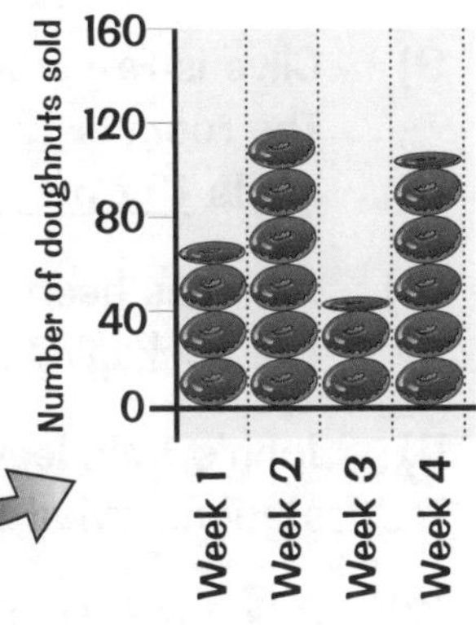

Pie Charts can be Used and Abused

This pie chart has four equal sectors. The angles for A, B, C and D are equal.

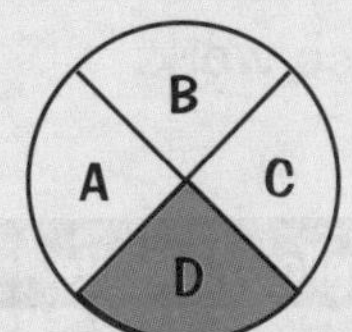

If the pie chart is made to look 3D it can be a bit misleading.

B
A
C
D

Sectors B and D now cover more of the page than A and C. They appear bigger to the eye even though all four are the same.

Revision Summary for Unit One — 2

QUESTION TIME AGAIN — use the methods covered in the second half of Section One to help you answer these questions.

1) Joe's bed is 3 feet 10 inches wide. His bedroom is 5 feet 3 inches wide. Will a bedside table that is 20 inches wide fit next to the bed?

2) What are the Three Steps of the Conversion Factor Method?

3) Kylie is on holiday in South Africa, where £1 = 12.12 rand. She pays 250 rand to go to a safari park. How much has she spent in pounds?

4) Jane is making pancakes. She has 0.7 litres of milk but needs 550 cm^3 according to the recipe. Does she have enough milk to make the pancakes?

5) 1 mile = 1.6 km. How many miles is 27 km? Give it to the nearest mile.

6) 1 kg = 2.2 lbs. Kevin is filling in a form to join the gym and needs to give his weight in kg. He knows he weighs 10 st 4 lbs. How much is this in kg?

7) A ship sets off from Port P on a bearing of 160°. Show its direction on the drawing opposite: Another ship sets off on a bearing of 240°. Show its direction too:

Port P

8) A plan of Alison's garden is shown on the right. Alison wants to put a fence around the perimeter of her garden, leaving only the gap that is shown. How many metres of fencing should Alison buy?

Gap
4 m
2 m
5 m
2 m
12 m

9) Clive is re-carpeting his lounge, which is rectangular. The room is 12 m long and 7 m wide. The carpet he wants costs £12 per m^2. How much will it cost Clive to carpet his lounge?

10) Jane has been asked to design packaging to hold 30 cm^3 of washing powder. The packaging must be a prism. Sketch a possible design for the box.

11) John's train leaves the station at 1.15 pm. He knows it takes him 25 mins to walk to the station. What is the latest time he should leave the house?

12) A film is 190 minutes long. It starts at 18.15. When will it finish?

13) In a frequency table what does $50 \le w < 60$ mean? Would you put 50 in this group? What about 60, would it go in this group or the next one up, $60 \le w < 70$?

14) For this set of numbers:
2, 6, 7, 12, 3, 7, 4, 15
a) Find the MODE
b) Find the MEDIAN
c) Find the MEAN
d) Find the RANGE

15) Fiona has carried out a traffic survey as part of her Geography course work. She wants to present the information in a pie chart.
a) Complete Fiona's table.
b) Draw the PIE CHART.

Colour	Blue	Red	Yellow	White	Totals:
Number of Cars	12	15	4	9	40
Angle on Pie Chart					360°

Multiplying by 10, 100, etc

You really should know the stuff on this page because:
a) it's nice 'n simple, and b) they're likely to test you on it in the Exam.

Whenever you multiply or divide numbers you need to follow these rules...

+ + makes +	+ − makes −
− + makes −	− − makes +

...see p.2 for examples.

1) To Multiply Any Number by 10

Move the Decimal Point ONE place BIGGER and if it's needed, ADD A ZERO on the end.

Examples:
23.6 × 10 = 236
345 × 10 = 3450
45.678 × 10 = 456.78

2) To Multiply Any Number by 100

Move the Decimal Point TWO places BIGGER and ADD ZEROS if necessary.

Examples:
296.5 × 100 = 29650
34 × 100 = 3400
2.543 × 100 = 254.3

3) To Multiply by 1000 or 10 000, the same rule applies:

Move the Decimal Point so many places BIGGER and ADD ZEROS if necessary.

Examples:
341 × 1000 = 341000
2.3542 × 10 000 = 23542

You always move the DECIMAL POINT this much:
1 place for 10, 2 places for 100,
3 places for 1000, 4 for 10 000 etc.

4) To Multiply by Numbers like 20, 300, 8000 etc.

MULTIPLY by 2 or 3 or 8 etc. FIRST, then move the Decimal Point so many places BIGGER (↷) according to how many noughts there are.

Example: To find 234 × 200, first multiply by 2 234 × 2 = 468,
then move the DP 2 places = 46800

Adding zeros when they're not needed? Tut, tut, noughty, noughty...

Just four multiplying methods to learn here — nothing too strenuous. For a bit of a workout, try these:

1) Work out a) 12.3 × 100 b) 345 × 10 c) 9.65 × 1000
2) Work out a) 2.4 × 20 b) 1.5 × 300 c) 60 × 3000

Dividing by 10, 100, etc

This is pretty easy stuff too. Just make sure you know it — that's all.

1) To Divide Any Number by 10

Move the Decimal Point ONE place SMALLER and if it's needed, REMOVE ZEROS after the decimal point.

Examples:
23.6 ÷ 10 = 2.36

340 ÷ 10 = 34.0

45.678 ÷ 10 = 4.5678

2) To Divide Any Number by 100

Move the Decimal Point TWO places SMALLER and REMOVE ZEROS after the decimal point.

Examples:
296.5 ÷ 100 = 2.965

340 ÷ 100 = 3.4

2543 ÷ 100 = 25.43

3) To Divide by 1000 or 10 000, the same rule applies:

Move the Decimal Point so many places SMALLER and REMOVE ZEROS after the decimal point.

Examples:
341 ÷ 1000 = 0.341

23 500 ÷ 10 000 = 2.35

You always move the DECIMAL POINT this much:
1 place for 10, 2 places for 100,
3 places for 1000, 4 for 10 000 etc.

4) To Divide by Numbers like 40, 300, 7000 etc.

DIVIDE by 4 or 3 or 7 etc. FIRST, then move the Decimal Point so many places SMALLER (i.e. to the left).

Example:
To find 960 ÷ 300, first divide by 3 960 ÷ 3 = 320,
then move the DP 2 places smaller = 3.2

With love to guide us, nothing can divide us...

... a great man once said. In other news, knowing how to divide by multiples of 10 will be very handy.

1) Work out a) 2.45 ÷ 10 b) 654.2 ÷ 100 c) 3.08 ÷ 1000
2) Work out a) 32 ÷ 20 b) 360 ÷ 30 c) 4000 ÷ 800

Addition and Subtraction

Imagine... stuck on a desert island, you build a boat out of coconut trees. Without a calculator, you couldn't subtract the trunks you needed from the number of trees, and now it's leaky (work with me here, ok?). But armed with this page, a stick and some damp sand, you'll be nice and dry. Phew.

Adding

1) Line up the units columns of each number.
2) Add up the columns from right to left.
3) Carry over any spare tens to the next column.

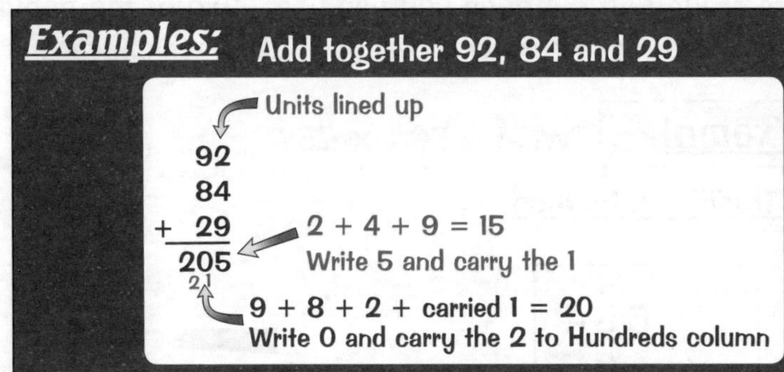

Subtracting

1) Line up the units columns of each number.
2) Working right to left, subtract the bottom number from the top number.
3) If the top number is smaller than the bottom number, borrow 10 from the left.

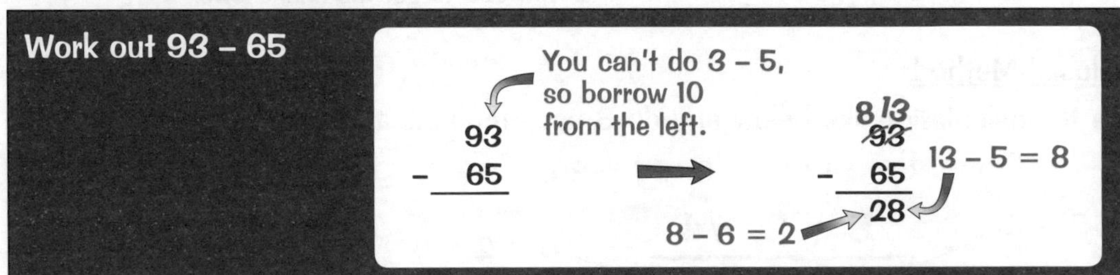

And With Decimals...

The method's just the same, but start instead by lining up the decimal points.

Work out 3.74 + 24.2 + 0.6.

Decimal points lined up

3.74
24.20
0.60
28.54

7 + 2 + 6 = 15
Write 5 and carry the 1

3 + 4 + 0 + the 1 carried over = 8

Bob has £8, but spends 26p on chewing-gum. How much is left?

Decimal points line up

£8.00
– £0.26

0 is smaller than 6 so you can't do 0 – 6

Borrow 10

7 10
£8.00
– £0.26

Borrow 10 again

7 9 10 10
£8.00
– £0.26
£7.74

9 – 2 = 7

10 – 6 = 4

Peter failed to tow the ship with his U-boat — he couldn't get sub-traction...

Ahem. Anyway, test your skills of pen-and-paper maths with these teasers:

1) When Ric was 10 he was 142 cm tall. Since then he has grown 29 cm.
   a) How tall is he now? b) How much taller must he be to be 190 cm tall?
2) I have 3 litres of water and drink 1.28 litres. How much is left?

Don't forget to include the units in your answer.

Multiplying Without a Calculator

You need to be really happy doing multiplications without a calculator — you'll definitely need to do it in your exam. So make sure you learn the methods on this page...

Multiplying Whole Numbers

There are lots of methods you can use. Two of the popular ones are shown below. Just make sure you can do it using whichever method you prefer...

Example "What is 564 × 25?"

The Traditional Method:

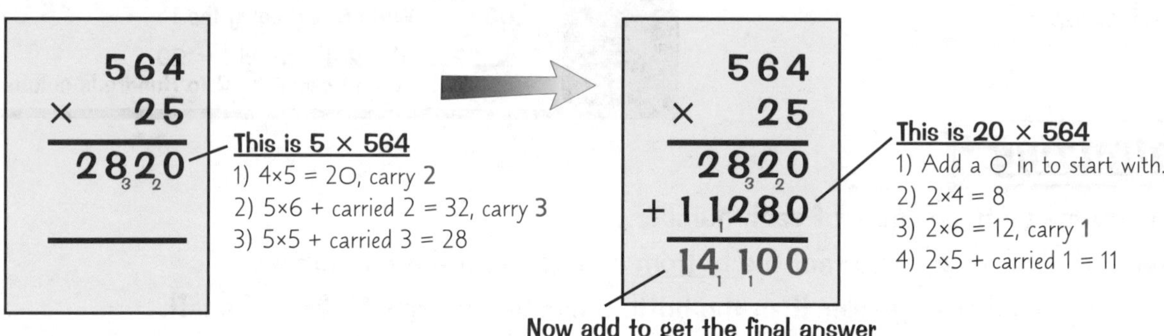

The 'Gelosia' Method:

Arrange the calculation like below and do 6 easy multiplications to fill up the grid...

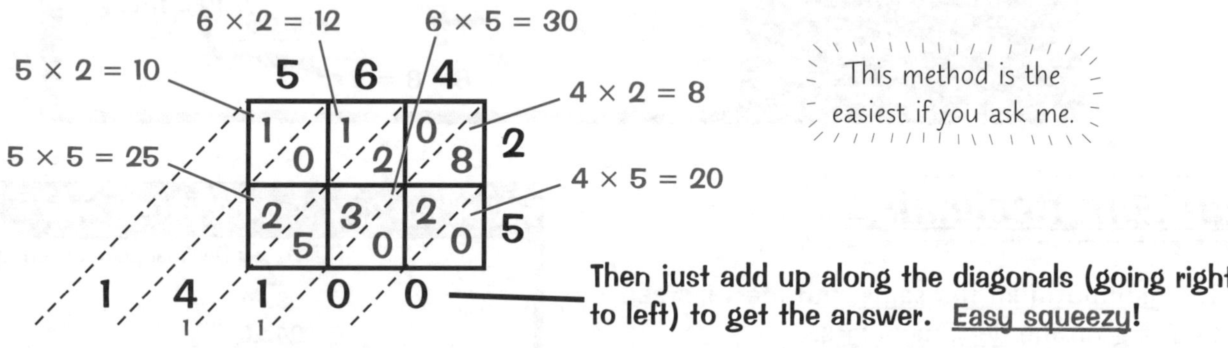

Multiplying Decimals

Learn this neat little method and you'll never be troubled by decimal points again... (probably).

1) To start with, forget about the decimal points and do the multiplication using whole numbers. (E.g. for 1.2 × 3.4 you'd do 12 × 34.)
2) Now count the total number of digits after the decimal points in the original numbers. (E.g. 1.2 and 3.4 — so that's 2 digits after the decimal point.)
3) Make the answer have the same number of decimal places.

Example: "Work out 5.64 × 2.5"

1) Ignore the d.p.s to start with: 564 × 25 = 14100
2) 5.64 × 2.5 has 3 digits after the decimal points.
3) So the answer is 14.1.

Work this out using one of the multiplication methods above.

Dividing Without a Calculator

OK, time for dividing now. Just remember, if you don't learn these basic methods, you'll find yourself in real trouble in the exam...

Dividing Whole Numbers

EXAMPLE: "What is 748 ÷ 22?"

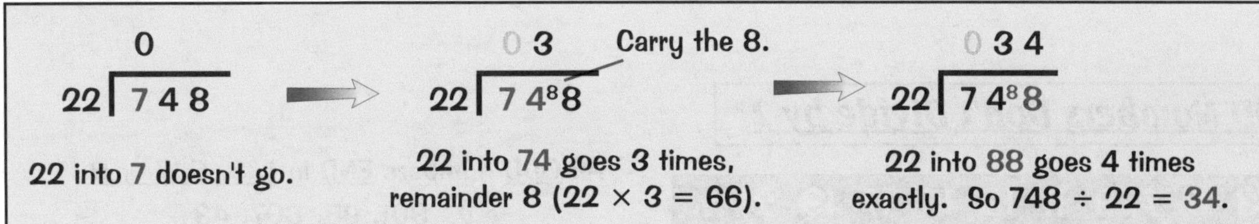

Dividing with Decimals

EXAMPLE: "What is 52.8 ÷ 3?"

Just set it out like the one we've just done but put the decimal point in the answer right above the one in the question...

1 — $3 \overline{)5^{2}2\,.\,8}$ — 3 into 5 goes once, carry the remainder of 2.

1 7 . — $3 \overline{)5^{2}2\,.\,^{1}8}$ — 3 into 22 goes 7 times, carry the remainder of 1.

1 7 . 6 — $3 \overline{)5^{2}2\,.\,^{1}8}$ — 3 into 18 goes 6 times exactly. So 52.8 ÷ 3 = 17.6.

EXAMPLE: "What is 83.6 ÷ 0.4?"

The trick with ones like this is to remember it's a fraction: $\frac{83.6}{0.4}$

Now you can get rid of the decimals by multiplying the top and bottom by 10 (turning it into an equivalent fraction): $\frac{83.6}{0.4} = \frac{836}{4}$

It's now a lovely decimal-free division that you know how to solve:

2 — $4 \overline{)8\,3\,6}$ — 4 into 8 goes twice.

2 0 — $4 \overline{)8\,3\,^{3}6}$ — 4 into 3 won't go so carry 3.

2 0 9 — $4 \overline{)8\,3\,^{3}6}$ — 4 into 36 goes 9 times so 83.6 ÷ 0.4 = 209.

Sums without calculators — less painful than standing on a plug barefoot...

Hmm, lots of info to take in there — it's really important that you learn all the methods on these two pages though. Have another read if you're still a bit unsure. Then try all of these without a calculator:

1) 28 × 12
2) 56 × 11
3) 104 × 8
4) 96 ÷ 8
5) 242 ÷ 2
6) 84 ÷ 7
7) 3.2 × 56
8) 33.6 ÷ 0.6
9) 69 ÷ 1.5
10) 43.2 ÷ 3.6

Special Number Sequences

You need to know all the types of number sequence on this page.
And as you'll find out, they're each special in their very own way. Bless.

EVEN Numbers all Divide by 2

2 4 6 8 10 12 14 16 18 20 ...

All EVEN numbers END in 0, 2, 4, 6 or 8
e.g. 200, 342, 576, 94

ODD Numbers Don't Divide by 2

1 3 5 7 9 11 13 15 17 19 21 ...

All ODD numbers END in 1, 3, 5, 7 or 9
e.g. 301, 95, 807, 43

SQUARE Numbers:

They're called SQUARE NUMBERS because they're like the areas of this pattern of squares:

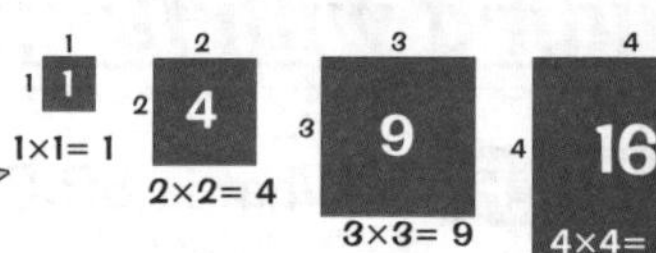

(1×1) (2×2) (3×3) (4×4) (5×5) (6×6) (7×7) (8×8) (9×9) (10×10) (11×11) (12×12) (13×13) (14×14) (15×15)

1 4 9 16 25 36 49 64 81 100 121 144 169 196 225...

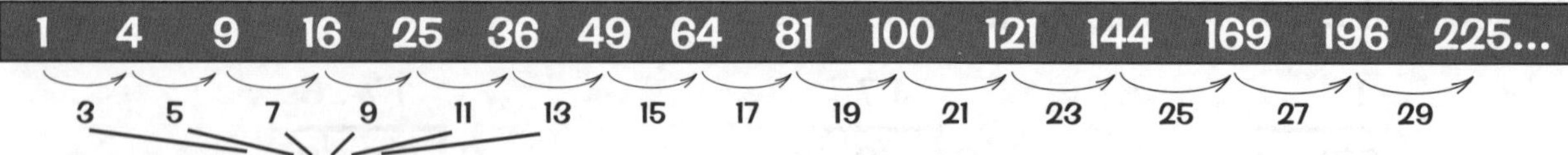

Note that the DIFFERENCES between the square numbers are all the ODD numbers.

CUBE Numbers:

They're called CUBE NUMBERS because they're like the volumes of this pattern of cubes.

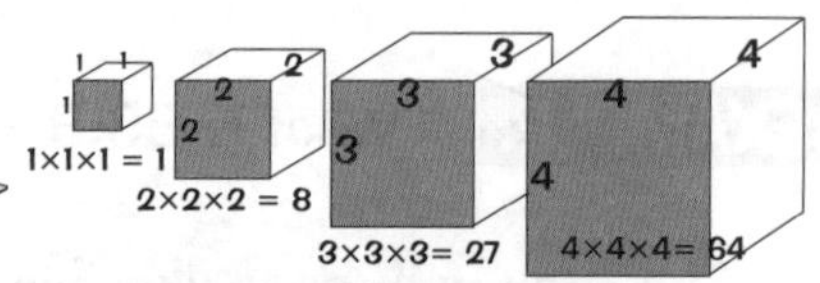

(1×1×1) (2×2×2) (3×3×3) (4×4×4) (5×5×5) (6×6×6) (7×7×7) (8×8×8) (9×9×9) (10×10×10)...

1 8 27 64 125 216 343 512 729 1000...

POWERS:

Powers are 'numbers multiplied by themselves so many times'
'Two to the power three' $= 2^3 = 2 \times 2 \times 2 = 8$

Here's the first few POWERS OF 2:

2 4 8 16 32...

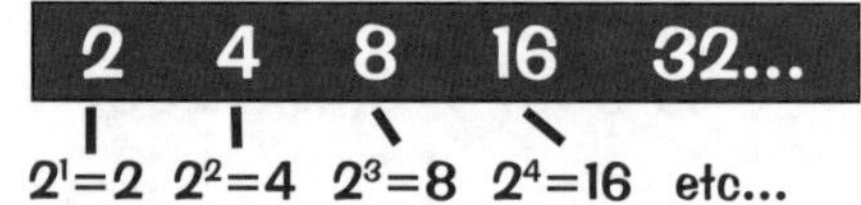

... and the first POWERS OF 10 (even easier):

10 100 1000 10 000 100 000...

$10^1=10$ $10^2=100$ $10^3=1000$ etc...

What do you do if your cube numbers are sad? Tell them they're special...

1) Cover up the page and then write down the first 15 numbers in all six sequences.
2) From this list of numbers: 23, 45, 56, 81, 25, 97, 134, 156, 125, 36, 1, 64
write down: a) all the even numbers b) all the odd numbers c) all the square numbers d) all the cube numbers e) all the powers of 2 or 10.

Prime Numbers

There's one more special number sequence you need to know about — the Prime Numbers...

1) Basically, PRIME Numbers Don't Divide by Anything

...and that's the best way to think of them. (Strictly, they divide by themselves and 1).
So Prime Numbers are all the numbers that DON'T come up in Times Tables:

2 3 5 7 11 13 17 19 23 29 31 37 ...

As you can see, they're an awkward-looking bunch (that's because they don't divide by anything!).
E.g.

The only numbers that multiply to give 7 are 1×7
The only numbers that multiply to give 31 are 1×31

In fact the only way to get ANY PRIME NUMBER is: $1 \times$ ITSELF

2) They End in 1, 3, 7 or 9

1) 1 is NOT a prime number.
2) The first four prime numbers are 2, 3, 5 and 7.
3) Prime numbers end in 1, 3, 7 or 9 (2 and 5 are the only exceptions to this rule).
4) But NOT ALL numbers ending in 1, 3, 7 or 9 are primes, as shown here: (Only the circled ones are primes)

(2)	(3)	(5)	(7)
(11)	(13)	(17)	(19)
21	(23)	27	(29)
(31)	33	(37)	39
(41)	(43)	(47)	49
51	(53)	57	(59)
(61)	63	(67)	69

3) How to FIND Prime Numbers – a very simple method

1) Since all primes (above 5) end in 1, 3, 7, or 9, then to find a prime number between say, 70 and 80, the only possibilities are: 71, 73, 77 and 79
2) Now, to find which of them ACTUALLY ARE primes you only need to divide each one by 3 and 7. If it doesn't divide exactly by either 3 or 7 then it's a prime. (This simple rule using just 3 and 7 is true for checking primes up to 120)

So, to find the primes between 70 and 80, just try dividing 71, 73, 77 and 79 by 3 and 7:

$71 \div 3 = 23.667$ $71 \div 7 = 10.143$ so 71 IS a prime number
(because it ends in 1, 3, 7 or 9 and it doesn't divide by 3 or 7)

$73 \div 3 = 24.333$ $73 \div 7 = 10.429$ so 73 IS a prime number

$79 \div 3 = 26.333$ $79 \div 7 = 11.286$ so 79 IS a prime number

$77 \div 3 = 25.667$ BUT: $77 \div 7 = 11$ — 11 is a whole number (or 'integer'),
so 77 is NOT a prime, because it divides by 7.

Two is the oddest prime of all — it's the only one that's even...

Learn all three sections above, then cover the page and write down everything you've just learned.
1) Write down the first 15 prime numbers (without looking them up).
2) Using the above method, find all the prime numbers between 90 and 110.

Multiples, Factors and Prime Factors

Hmm, the words above look important. Panic ye not, explanations and examples are on their way...

Multiples

The MULTIPLES of a number are simply its TIMES TABLE:

E.g. the multiples of 13 are: 13 26 39 52 65 78 91 104 ...

Factors

The FACTORS of a number are all the numbers that DIVIDE INTO IT. There's a special way to find them:

EXAMPLE 1 "Find ALL the factors of 24".

Start off with 1× the number itself, then try 2×, then 3× and so on, listing the pairs in rows like this. Try each one in turn and put a dash if it doesn't divide exactly. Eventually, when you get a number repeated, you stop.

Increasing by 1 each time

1 × 24
2 × 12
3 × 8
4 × 6
5 × –
6 × 4

So the FACTORS OF 24 are
1, 2, 3, 4, 6, 8, 12, 24

This method guarantees you find them ALL — but don't forget 1 and 24!

EXAMPLE 2 "Find the factors of 64".

Check each one in turn, to see if it divides or not.

1 × 64
2 × 32
3 × –
4 × 16
5 × –
6 × –
7 × –
8 × 8 — The 8 has repeated so stop here.

So the FACTORS OF 64 are
1, 2, 4, 8, 16, 32, 64

Finding Prime Factors — The Factor Tree

Any number can be broken down into a string of PRIME NUMBERS all multiplied together — this is called 'Expressing it as a product of prime factors'.

To be honest it's pretty tedious – but it's in the Exam, and it's not difficult so long as you know what it is.

The mildly entertaining 'Factor Tree' method is best, where you start at the top and split your number off into factors as shown. Each time you get a prime, you ring it and you finally end up with all the prime factors, which you can then arrange in order.

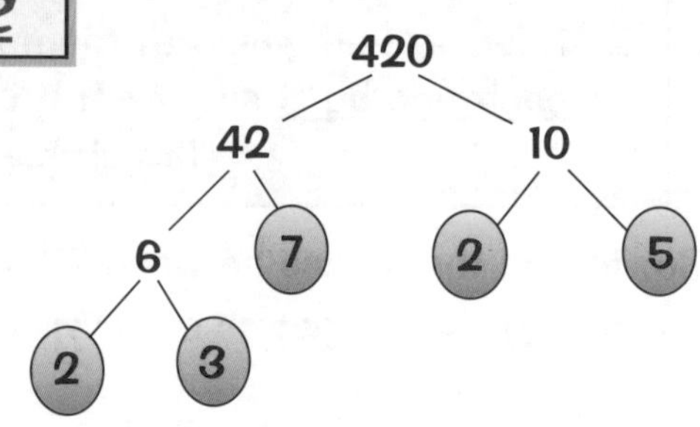

So, 'As a product of prime factors',
420 = 2 × 2 × 3 × 5 × 7
(or $2^2 \times 3 \times 5 \times 7$ in index form)

"I run marathons, cycle everyday..." — quote from a factor in his prime...

Learn what multiples, factors and prime factors are, and how to find them. Turn over and write it down.

1) List the first 10 multiples of 7, and the first 10 multiples of 9.
2) List all the factors of 36 and all the factors of 84.
3) Express as a product of prime factors: a) 990 b) 160.

LCM and HCF

Two big fancy names but don't be put off — they're both really easy.

LCM — 'Least Common Multiple'

'Least Common Multiple' — sure, it sounds kind of complicated but all it means is this:

The SMALLEST number that will DIVIDE BY ALL the numbers in question.

The least common multiple is sometimes called the lowest common multiple.

Method

1) LIST the MULTIPLES of ALL the numbers.
2) Find the SMALLEST one that's in ALL the lists.
3) Easy peasy innit.

Example Find the least common multiple (LCM) of 6 and 7.

Multiples of 6 are: 6, 12, 18, 24, 30, 36, (42), 48, 54, 60, 66, ...
Multiples of 7 are: 7, 14, 21, 28, 35, (42), 49, 56, 63, 70, 77, ...

So the least common multiple (LCM) of 6 and 7 is 42. Told you it was easy.

HCF — 'Highest Common Factor'

'Highest Common Factor' — all it means is this:

The BIGGEST number that will DIVIDE INTO ALL the numbers in question.

Method

1) LIST the FACTORS of all the numbers.
2) Find the BIGGEST one that's in ALL the lists.
3) Easy peasy innit.

(Use the method on p.48 to work out the factors.)

Example Find the highest common factor (HCF) of 36, 54, and 72.

Factors of 36 are: 1, 2, 3, 4, 6, 9, 12, (18), 36
Factors of 54 are: 1, 2, 3, 6, 9, (18), 27, 54
Factors of 72 are: 1, 2, 3, 4, 6, 8, 9, 12, (18), 24, 36, 72

So the highest common factor (HCF) of 36, 54 and 72 is 18. Told you it was easy.

Just take care listing the factors — make sure you use the proper method (as shown on the previous page) or you'll miss one and blow the whole thing out of the water.

Highest common revision related injury — papercuts...

Make sure you're happy with what LCM and HCF are, and how to find them. Then have a go at these chaps:

1) List the first 10 multiples of 8, and the first 10 multiples of 9. What's their LCM?
2) List all the factors of 56 and all the factors of 104. What's their HCF?
3) What's the Least Common Multiple of 7 and 9?
4) What's the Highest Common Factor of 36 and 84?

Powers

Right. LEARN THIS PAGE, then PEEL ME SOME GRAPES and IRON MY SHIRTS.
Sorry, I think the power's gone to my head...

Powers are a very Useful Shorthand

$2\times2\times2\times2\times2\times2\times2 = 2^7$ ('two to the power 7')
$7\times7 = 7^2$ ('7 squared')
$6\times6\times6\times6\times6 = 6^5$ ('Six to the power 5')
$4\times4\times4 = 4^3$ ('four cubed')

That bit is easy to remember. Unfortunately, there are FIVE SPECIAL RULES for powers that are not quite so easy, but you do need to know them for the Exam:

The Five Rules

The first two only work for powers of the SAME NUMBER.

1) When MULTIPLYING, you ADD the powers.

e.g. $3^4 \times 3^6 = 3^{4+6} = 3^{10}$ $\quad 8^3 \times 8^5 = 8^{3+5} = 8^8$

2) When DIVIDING, you SUBTRACT the powers.

e.g. $5^4 \div 5^2 = 5^{4-2} = 5^2$ $\quad 12^8/12^3 = 12^{8-3} = 12^5$

3) When RAISING one power to another, you MULTIPLY the powers.

e.g. $(3^2)^4 = 3^{2\times4} = 3^8$, $(5^4)^6 = 5^{24}$

4) $X^1 = X$, ANYTHING TO THE POWER 1 is just ITSELF

e.g. $3^1 = 3$, $\quad 6 \times 6^3 = 6^4$, $\quad 4^3 \div 4^2 = 4^{3-2} = 4^1 = 4$

5) $1^x = 1$, 1 TO ANY POWER is still just 1

e.g. $1^{23} = 1$ $\quad 1^{89} = 1$ $\quad 1^2 = 1$ $\quad 1^{1012} = 1$

"I've got the power! oh, oh, oh, oh..." Oh no, I'm feeling kinda ninetees...

Some say you should learn the Five Rules for Powers. Then turn over and write it all down.
Well, I say "Keep trying until you can do it! Then cover the page and apply the rules to simplify these."

1) a) $3^2 \times 3^6$ b) $4^3 \div 4^2$ c) $(8^3)^4$ d) $(3^2 \times 3^3 \times 1^6) / 3^5$ e) $7^3 \times 7 \times 7^2$

2) a) $5^2 \times 5^7 \times 5^3$ b) $(2^5 \times 2 \times 2^6) \div (2^3 \times 2^4)$

Roots and Reciprocals

Take a deep breath, and get ready to tackle this page. Good luck with it, I'll be rootin' for ya...

Square Roots

'Squared' means 'times by itself' : $P^2 = P \times P$
— SQUARE ROOT is the reverse process.

The best way to think of it is this:

'Square Root' means 'What Number Times by Itself gives...'

Example: 'Find the square root of 49' (i.e. 'Find $\sqrt{49}$')

To do this you should say "what number times by itself gives... 49?"

And the answer of course is 7.

Square Roots can be Positive or Negative

When you take the square root of a number, the answer can actually be positive or negative... you always have a positive and negative version of the same number.

E.g. $x^2 = 4$ gives $x = \pm\sqrt{4} = +2$ or -2

To understand why, look at what happens when you work backwards by squaring the answers: $2^2 = 2 \times 2 = 4$ but also $(-2)^2 = (-2) \times (-2) = 4$

Cube Roots

'Cubed' means 'times by itself three times' : $T^3 = T \times T \times T$
— CUBE ROOT is the reverse process.

'Cube Root' means 'What Number Times by Itself THREE TIMES gives...'

Example: "Find the cube root of 64" (i.e 'Find $\sqrt[3]{64}$')

Well, strictly there are only two × signs, but you know what I mean.

You should say "What number times by itself three times gives... 64?"

And after a few guesses, the answer is 4.

(Note — unlike square roots, there's only ever one answer.)

Reciprocals — Learn these 4 Facts

1) The reciprocal of a number is 'one over' the number. → The reciprocal of 5 = $\frac{1}{5}$.
2) You can find the reciprocal of a fraction by turning it upside down. → The reciprocal of $\frac{3}{8} = \frac{8}{3}$.
3) A number multiplied by its reciprocal gives 1. → $\frac{6}{7} \times \frac{7}{6} = 1$
4) 0 has no reciprocal because you can't divide anything by 0.

"Cue brute", that's what I call Charley when I play him at snooker...

LEARN the 2 statements in the blue boxes, the methods for finding the roots and the 4 facts about reciprocals. Then turn the page and write it all down.

1) a) If $g^2 = 36$, find g. b) If $b^3 = 64$, find b. c) If $4 \times r^2 = 36$, find r. d) If $4/r = 8$, find r.

Fractions, Decimals and Percentages

Back in Unit 1 we had a joyous time learning about fractions decimals and percentages. And I know it left you wanting more. Well, as a special treat, just for you, here they come again...

Fractions, Decimals and Percentages are Interchangeable

You need to be able to <u>convert</u> fractions into decimals, decimals into percentages, percentages into fractions, etc. etc. If you look back to page 10 you'll see a big old table showing you some easy conversions. The more of those conversions you learn, the better — but for those that you <u>don't know</u>, you must <u>also learn</u> how to <u>convert</u> between the three types. These are the methods:

Fraction —Divide→ **Decimal** —× by 100→ **Percentage**

e.g. $\frac{1}{2}$ is $1 \div 2$ = 0.5 e.g. 0.5×100 = 50%

Fraction ←The tricky one— **Decimal** ←÷ by 100— **Percentage**

<u>Converting decimals to fractions</u> is only possible for <u>exact decimals</u> that haven't been rounded off. It's simple enough, but it's best illustrated by examples — see below. You should be able to work out what the simple rule is.

$0.6 = \frac{6}{10}$ $0.3 = \frac{3}{10}$ $0.7 = \frac{7}{10}$ $0.x = \frac{x}{10}$ etc.

Some of these can then be <u>cancelled down</u>.

$0.12 = \frac{12}{100}$ $0.78 = \frac{78}{100}$ $0.45 = \frac{45}{100}$ $0.05 = \frac{5}{100}$ etc.

$0.345 = \frac{345}{1000}$ $0.908 = \frac{908}{1000}$ $0.024 = \frac{24}{1000}$ $0.xyz = \frac{xyz}{1000}$ etc.

<u>Recurring</u> decimals like 0.3333... are all actually just <u>exact fractions</u> in disguise. But don't worry, you don't need to know how to convert them back into fractions.

Unfortunately, you need to know all the stuff on fractions, decimals and percentages that you learned for Unit 1, so have a look back at pages 10-15 and check you still know it.

Not fractions again — they're like a recurring nightmare...

Learn the 4 conversion processes. Then it's time to break into a mild sweat...

1) Turn the following decimals into fractions and reduce to their simplest form.

a) 0.6 b) 0.02 c) 0.77 d) 0.555 e) 5.6

Fractions, Decimals and Percentages

Putting numbers in size order — sounds pretty straightforward. But what if they're fractions, or decimals, or a combination of fractions and percentages... Fear not, it's still pretty straightforward.

Ordering Fractions — Put them over the Same No.

E.g. Put these fractions in ascending order of size: $\frac{8}{3}, \frac{6}{4}, \frac{12}{5}$

① First, to find the new denominator, just find the LCM (see p49) of the denominators: LCM of 3, 4 and 5 is 60

② Then change each fraction so it's over the new number: $\frac{8}{3} = \frac{160}{60}$ (×20), $\frac{6}{4} = \frac{90}{60}$ (×15), $\frac{12}{5} = \frac{144}{60}$ (×12)

③ Now they're easy to write in order: $\frac{90}{60}, \frac{144}{60}, \frac{160}{60}$ or $\frac{6}{4}, \frac{12}{5}, \frac{8}{3}$.

Ordering Decimals

For decimals, do the whole-number bit first before looking at what's after the point. With numbers between 0 and 1, first group them by the number of 0s at the start. The group with the most 0s at the start comes first, so for the numbers 0.03, 0.14, 0.7, 0.0026, 0.098, 0.007 and 0.531:

(those with 2 initial 0s,	then those with 1 initial 0,	then those with no initial 0s.)
0.0026 0.007	0.03 0.098	0.14 0.531 0.7

Once they're in groups, just order them by comparing the first non-zero digits.
(If the first digits are the same, look at the next digit along instead.)

Comparing Fractions, Decimals and Percentages

Comparing fractions, decimals and percentages is dead easy. All you have to do is convert them all to be the same type of number, e.g. make them all percentages.

Example: Four fifths of visitors to Harry's restaurant 'Meat Feast' reported that they were satisfied with the service they'd received. 78% of visitors to his restaurant 'Veggie Haven' stated that they were satisfied. Which restaurant had the greater rate of customer satisfaction?

Answer: $\frac{4}{5} = 80\%$, so customer satisfaction is higher at Meat Feast.

That pesky LCM crops up here too — this is an outrage...

Sadly you've got to be able to mix and match all the stuff you're learning. Horrific, I know. Now you know how to order fractions, decimals and percentages try the questions below.

1) Order the following fractions: $\frac{11}{15}, \frac{3}{5}, \frac{2}{3}$

2) Order the following values: 23%, $\frac{6}{8}$, 47%, $\frac{3}{12}$

Fractions and Estimating Calculations

Here are some more ways to cope with fraction calculations without your beloved calculator.

Fraction Calculations

1) Multiplying — easy

Multiply top and bottom separately:

$$\frac{3}{5} \times \frac{4}{7} = \frac{3 \times 4}{5 \times 7} = \frac{12}{35}$$

2) Dividing — quite easy

Turn the 2nd fraction UPSIDE DOWN and then multiply:

$$\frac{3}{4} \div \frac{1}{3} = \frac{3}{4} \times \frac{3}{1} = \frac{3 \times 3}{4 \times 1} = \frac{9}{4}$$

3) Adding, Subtracting — fraught

Add or subtract TOP LINES ONLY but only if the denominators (bottom numbers) are the same.

(If they're not, you have to make them the same — see top of previous page).

$$\frac{2}{6} + \frac{1}{6} = \frac{3}{6}$$

$$\frac{5}{7} - \frac{3}{7} = \frac{2}{7}$$

There's more on fractions on page 11.

Estimating Calculations

As long as you realise what's expected, this is VERY EASY. People get confused because they over-complicate it. To estimate something this is all you do:

1) ROUND EVERYTHING OFF to nice easy CONVENIENT NUMBERS.
2) Then WORK OUT THE ANSWER using those nice easy numbers — and that's it!

Rounding numbers was covered in Unit 1, but you need to know it for Unit 2 as well — see p.6-7.

You don't worry about the answer being 'wrong', because we're only trying to get a rough idea of the size of the proper answer, e.g. is it about 20 or about 200?
Don't forget though, in the Exam you'll need to show all the steps you've done, to prove you didn't just use a calculator.

Example: ESTIMATE the value of $\frac{127 + 49}{56.5}$ showing all your working.

ANSWER: $\frac{127 + 49}{56.5} \approx \frac{130 + 50}{60} = \frac{180}{60} = 3$ ("≈" means "roughly equal to")

Don't underestimate the importance of eating biscuits when revising...

Almost done with fractions now, I promise. Just have a quick go at these questions...

1) a) $\frac{3}{8} \times \frac{5}{12}$ b) $\frac{4}{5} \div \frac{7}{8}$ c) $\frac{3}{4} + \frac{2}{5}$ d) $\frac{2}{5} - \frac{3}{8}$ e) $4\frac{1}{9} + 2\frac{2}{27}$

Change mixed fractions to top heavy fractions first e.g. $2\frac{2}{27} = \frac{56}{27}$

2) Estimate the value of $\frac{47 + 154}{19}$

X and Y Coordinates

Graph questions can actually be quite fun. OK, maybe not fun exactly, but better than hopping blindfolded through a hail storm in just your pants. First, you need to get a grip of the basics...

The Four Quadrants

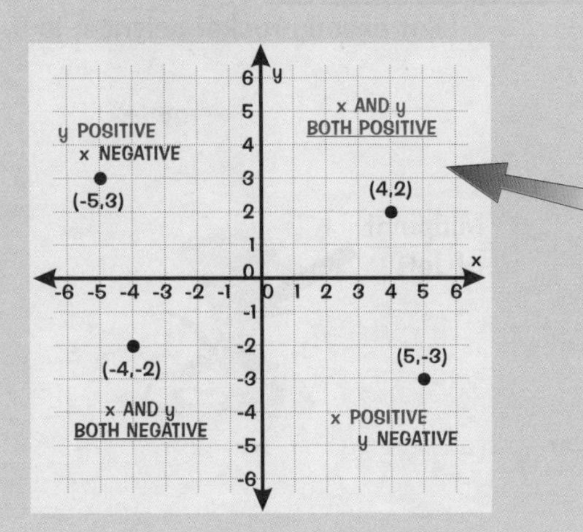

A graph has four different regions where the x- and y- coordinates are either positive or negative.

This is the easiest region by far because here ALL THE COORDINATES ARE POSITIVE.

You have to be dead careful in the OTHER REGIONS though, because the x- and y- coordinates could be negative, and that always makes life much more difficult.

X, Y Coordinates — Getting them in the Right Order

You must always give COORDINATES in brackets like this: (x, y)
And you always have to be real careful to get them the right way round, x first, then y.

Here are THREE POINTS to help you remember:

(x , y)

1) The two coordinates are always in ALPHABETICAL ORDER, x then y.
2) x is always the flat axis going ACROSS the page.
   In other words 'x is a..cross' Get it — x is a '×'. (Hilarious isn't it)
3) Remember it's always IN THE HOUSE (→) and then UP THE STAIRS (↑)
   so it's ALONG first and then UP, i.e. x-coordinate first, and then y-coordinate.

'x' is across... and 'y'?... because it's a cross... No, 'y'?...

Ah, a nice easy page. Make sure you learn the 3 Rules for getting x and y the right way round. Then turn over and write it all down.
Write down the coordinates of the letters A to H on this graph:

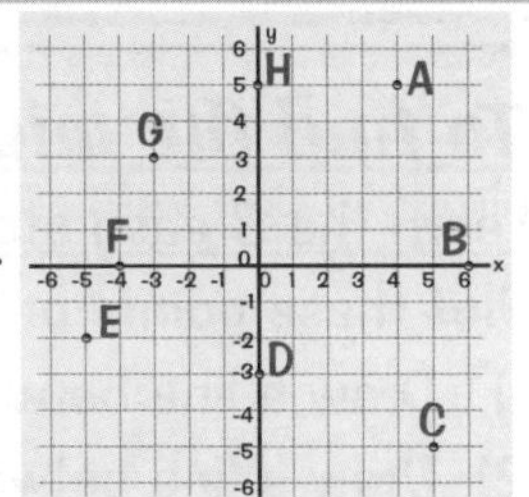

Midpoint of a Line Segment

Man, that's one scary sounding title, but don't let it fool you.
When you get down to it, finding the midpoint is just a spot of <u>adding</u> and <u>dividing by two</u>.

The 'Midpoint' is just the Middle of the Line

The '<u>MIDPOINT OF A LINE SEGMENT</u>' is the <u>POINT THAT'S BANG IN THE MIDDLE</u> of it.

(Not exactly rocket science, is it...)

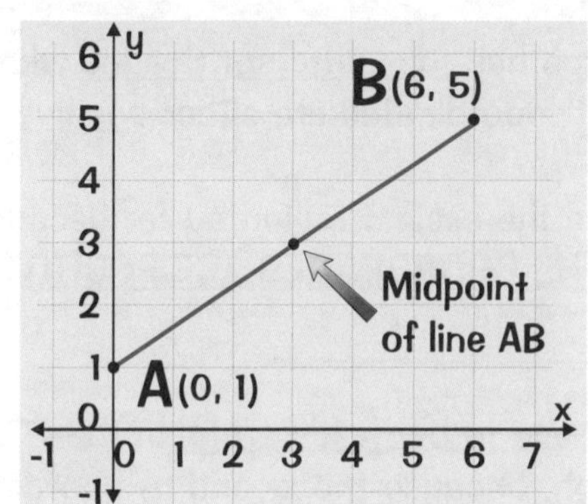

Find the Coordinates of a Midpoint

The only thing you really need to know about midpoints is how to find the coordinates of one.

And it's pretty easy. The x-coordinate of the midpoint is the average of the x-coordinates of the end points — and the same goes for the y-coordinates.

<u>EXAMPLE</u>: "A and B have coordinates (2,1) and (6,3)
Find the midpoint of the line AB."

B(6, 3)
A (2, 1) Midpoint

Then follow these <u>THREE EASY STEPS</u>...

1) Find the <u>average</u> of the <u>x-coordinates</u> of the two points.
2) Find the <u>average</u> of the <u>y-coordinates</u> of the two points.
3) Plonk them in <u>brackets</u>.

Average of x-coordinates
$= (2 + 6) \div 2 = \underline{4}$

Average of y-coordinates
$= (1 + 3) \div 2 = \underline{2}$

Plonk them in brackets
(x-coordinate first): $(\underline{4}, \underline{2})$

To find the midpoint — average, average, plonk

<u>Learn the 3 easy steps</u> for finding midpoints. Close the book and <u>write them down</u>.
Plot these points on some graph paper: A(1,4), B(5,6), C(3,2), D(7,0).

1) Draw a line between points A and B and find the midpoint of the line AB.
2) Draw a line between points C and D and find the midpoint of line CD.

Straight Line Graphs

If you thought eye-spy was fun, wait 'til you play 'recognise the straight line graph from its equation'.

Horizontal and Vertical lines: "x = a" and "y = b"

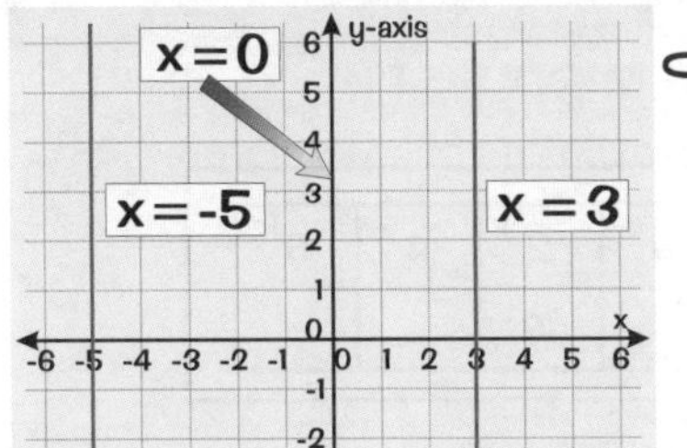

x = a is a vertical line through 'a' on the x-axis

y = a is a horizontal line through 'a' on the y-axis

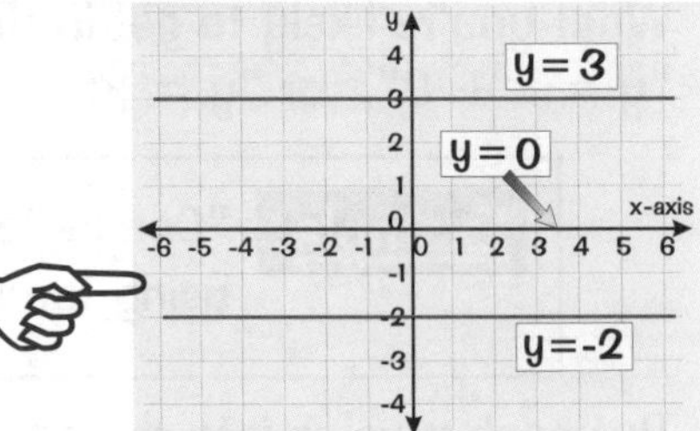

Don't forget: the y-axis is also the line x=0

Don't forget: the x-axis is also the line y=0

The Main Diagonals: "y = x" and "y = –x"

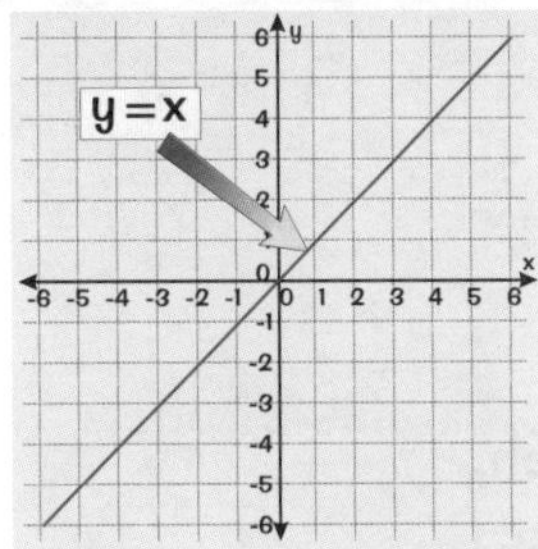

'y = x' is the main diagonal that goes UPHILL from left to right.

'y = -x' is the main diagonal that goes DOWNHILL from left to right.

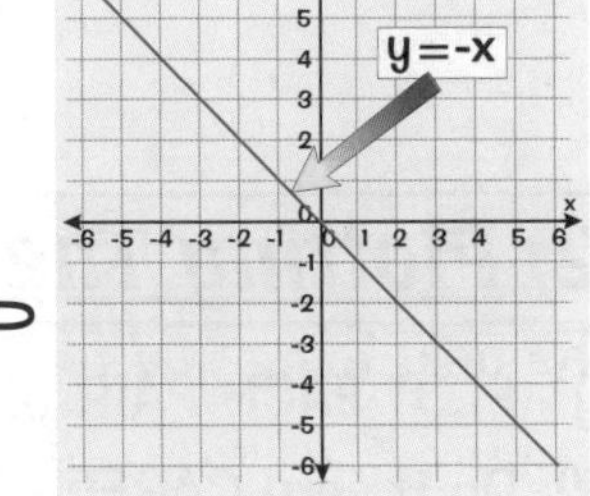

Other Sloping Lines Through the origin: "y = ax" and "y = –ax"

y = ax and y = -ax are the equations for A SLOPING LINE THROUGH THE ORIGIN.

The value of 'a' (known as the gradient) tells you the steepness of the line. The bigger 'a' is, the steeper the slope. A MINUS SIGN tells you it slopes DOWNHILL.

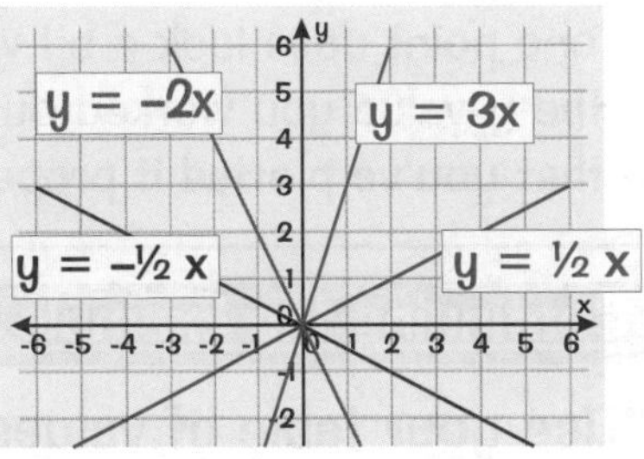

All Other Straight Lines

Other straight-line equations are a little more complicated. The next page shows you how to draw them, but the first step is identifying them in the first place.

Remember: All straight line equations just contain 'something x, something y, and a number'.

Straight lines:	
$x - y = 0$	$y = 2 + 3x$
$2y - 4x = 7$	$4x - 3 = 5y$
$3y + 3x = 12$	$6y - x - 7 = 0$

NOT straight lines:	
$y = x^3 + 3$	$2y - 1/x = 7$
$1/y + 1/x = 2$	$x(3 - 2y) = 3$
$x^2 = 4 - y$	$xy + 3 = 0$

My favourite line's y = 3x, it gets the chicks every time...

OK, maybe not every time, but it's still worth learning all this stuff. When you think you know it, turn over the page and write down everything you've learned.

Straight Line Graphs

Strap on a beret, grab a pencil and let's get arty (well, graphy at least) — it's graph drawing time.

1) Doing the Table of Values

1) What you're likely to get in the Exam is an equation such as "$y = x + 3$", or "$y = 3x + 2$" and a half-finished table of values:

Example: "Complete this table of values, using the equation $y = 2x - 7$"

x	-2	0	2	4	6
y	-11		-3		

2) Put each x-value into the equation and work out the corresponding y-values.
E.g. For $x = 0$, $y = 2x - 7 = (2 \times 0) - 7 = 0 - 7 = -7$, etc...

...until you get this:

x	-2	0	2	4	6
y	-11	-7	-3	1	5

2) Plotting The Points and Drawing The Graph

1) PLOT EACH PAIR of x- and y- values from the table as a point on the graph.
2) Do it very CAREFULLY — and don't mix up the x- and y-values. (See P.55)
3) The points will always form A DEAD STRAIGHT LINE.

NEVER let one point drag your line off in some ridiculous direction. You never get SPIKES – only MISTAKES.

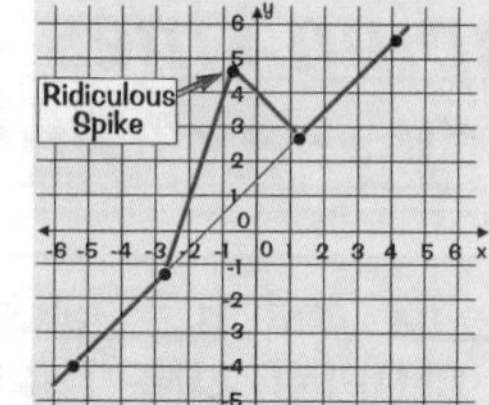

4) If one point does look a bit wacky, check 2 things:
– the y-value you worked out in the table
– that you've plotted it properly!

Continuing the Example from part 1):

"Use your table of values to plot the graph of $y = 2x - 7$"

Simple — plot each point carefully, then you should be able to draw a nice STRAIGHT LINE through all the points.

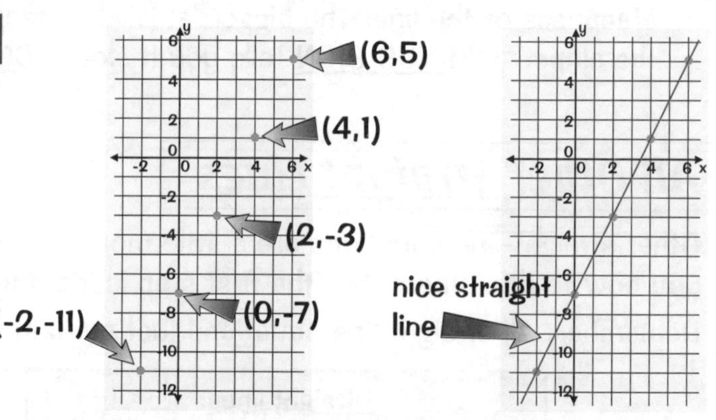

Careful plotting — the key to perfect straight lines and world domination...

... mwah ha ha ha. Learn this page, then have a go at the questions below.

1) Complete this table of values for the equation: $y = x - 2$
2) Then plot the points on graph paper and draw the graph.

x	-4	-2	-1	0	1	2	4
y	-6			-2			

Straight Line Graphs — Gradients

Time to hit the slopes. Well, find them anyway...

Finding the Gradient

1) Find TWO ACCURATE POINTS and COMPLETE THE TRIANGLE

Both points should be in the upper right quadrant if possible (to keep all the numbers positive).

①

Two accurate Points

Change in y

Change in x

2) Find the CHANGE IN Y and the CHANGE IN X

Make sure you subtract the x coords. the same way round as you do the y coords.
E.g. y coord. of pt A – y coord. of pt B
and x coord of pt A – x coord of pt B

② Change in y = 50 – 10 = 40
Change in x = 8 – 1 = 7

3) LEARN this formula, and use it:

$$\text{GRADIENT} = \frac{\text{CHANGE IN Y}}{\text{CHANGE IN X}}$$

③ Gradient = $\frac{40}{7}$ = 5.7

4) Check the SIGN'S right.

If it slopes UPHILL left → right (↗) then it's positive
If it slopes DOWNHILL left → right (↘) then it's negative

④ As the graph goes UPHILL, the gradient is positive. So 5.7 is correct, not -5.7

If you subtracted the coordinates the right way round, the sign should be correct. If it's not, go back and check what you've done.

Parallel Lines

1) The equation of a straight line is $y = mx + c$ (see next pg.) where m is the gradient and c is the y-intercept.

2) Parallel lines have the same value of m, i.e. the same gradient. So the lines: $y = 2x + 3$, $y = 2x$ and $y = 2x - 4$ are all parallel.

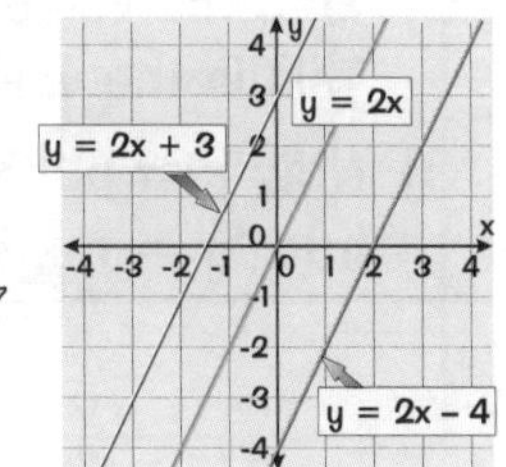

Finding gradients is often an uphill battle...

Learn the four steps for finding gradients then turn over and write them down from memory. Fun times.

1) Plot these 3 points on a graph: (0,3) (2,0) (5,-4.5) and then join them up with a straight line. Now carefully apply the four steps to find the gradient of the line.

Straight Line Graphs — y = mx + c

$y = mx + c$ is the general equation for a straight line graph, and you need to remember:

'm' is equal to the GRADIENT of the graph

'c' is the value WHERE IT CROSSES THE Y-AXIS and is called the Y-INTERCEPT.

1) Drawing a Straight Line using "y = mx + c"

The main thing is being able to identify 'm' and 'c' and knowing what to do with them:
BUT WATCH OUT — people often mix up 'm' and 'c', especially with say, '$y = 5 + 2x$'
REMEMBER: 'm' is the number IN FRONT OF X and 'c' is the number ON ITS OWN.

Method

1) Get the equation into the form '$y = mx + c$'.
2) Identify 'm' and 'c' carefully.
3) Put a dot on the y-axis at the value of c.
4) Then go along one unit and up or down by the value of m and make another dot.
5) Repeat the same 'step' in both directions as shown:
6) Finally check that the gradient LOOKS RIGHT.

y = 2x +1

START HERE

m=+2 so it's UP 2 units

ALWAYS along ONE Unit →

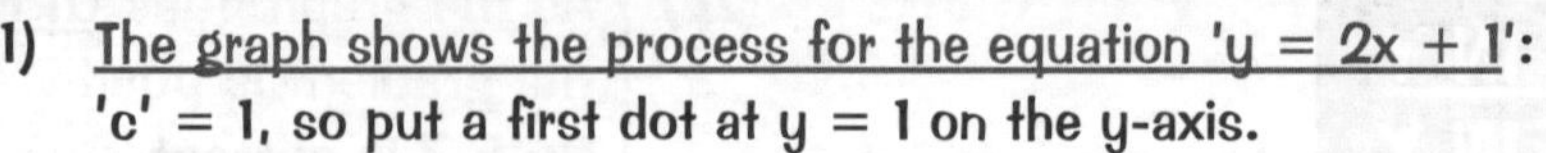

1) The graph shows the process for the equation '$y = 2x + 1$':
   'c' = 1, so put a first dot at y = 1 on the y-axis.
2) Go along 1 unit → and then up by 2 because 'm' = +2.
3) Repeat the same step, 1 → 2 in both directions. (i.e. 1 ← 2 ↓ the other way)
4) CHECK: a gradient of +2 should be quite steep and uphill left to right — which it is.

2) Finding the Equation Of a Straight Line Graph

THIS IS EASY:

1) Find where the graph CROSSES THE Y-AXIS. This is the value of 'c'.
2) Find the value of the GRADIENT (see p.59). This is the value of 'm'.
3) Now just put these values for 'm' and 'c' into '$y = mx + c$' — and there you have it!

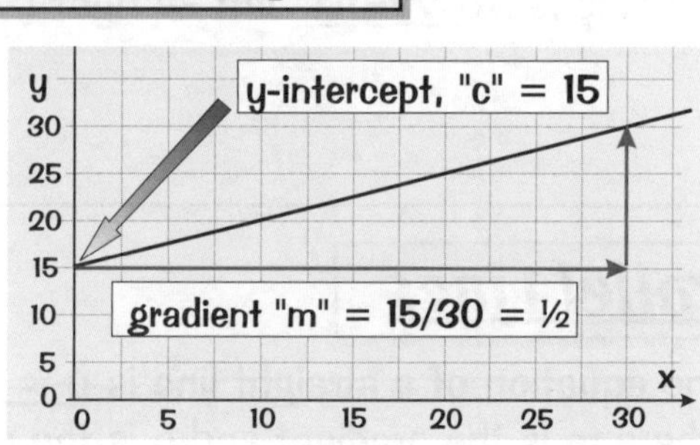

For the graph shown here, m = ½ and c = 15 so '$y = mx + c$' becomes '$y = \frac{1}{2}x + 15$'

Remember y = mx + c — it'll keep you on the straight and narrow...

That, and remembering the 2 METHODS for drawing the lines and finding the equations. Once you think you've got it, have a go at the questions below.

1) Using '$y = mx + c$' draw the graphs of $y = x - 3$ and $y = 4 - 2x$.
2) Using '$y = mx + c$' find the equations of these 3 graphs

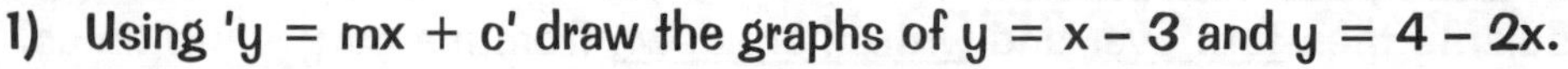

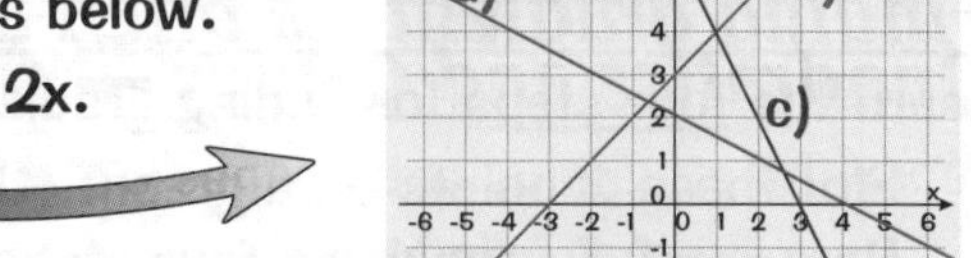

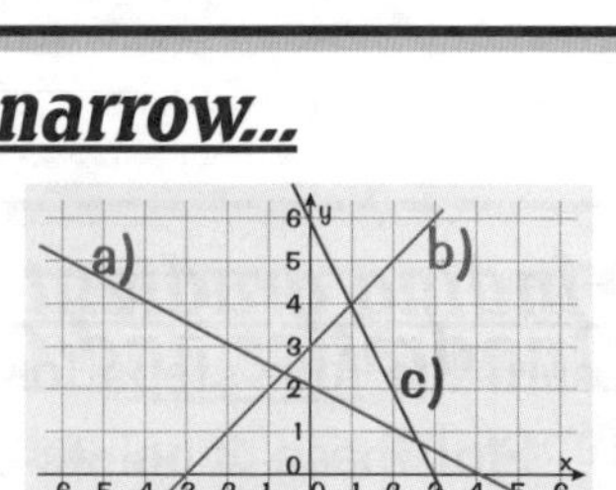

Quadratic and Cubic Graphs

Straight line graphs are all very well and good, but they're not exactly exciting. What you really need to keep you on the edge of your seat is some graphs with curves — that's the stuff we're really after. Step forward quadratic and cubic graphs.

x^2 BUCKET SHAPES: $y = ax^2 + bx + c$ (where b and/or c can be zero)

Equations with an x^2 term in them are called quadratic equations. The graphs of these equations always have the same SYMMETRICAL bucket shape and are imaginatively called quadratic graphs.

If the x^2 bit is positive (i.e. $+x^2$) the bucket is the normal way up, but if the x^2 bit has a "minus" in front of it (i.e. $-x^2$) then the bucket is upside down.

The graphs get steeper and steeper but never vertical — remember this when you're drawing them.

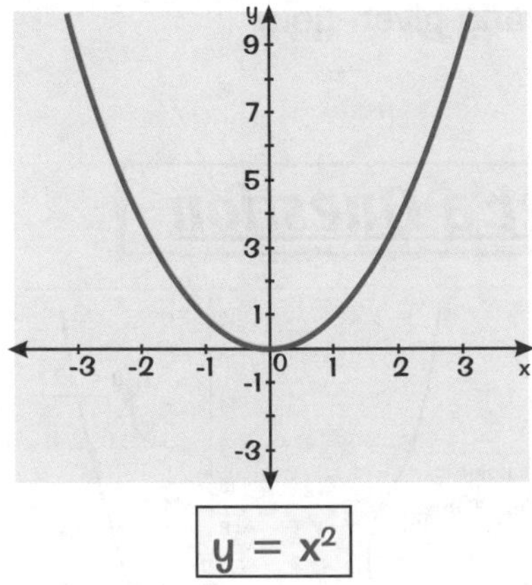

$y = x^2$

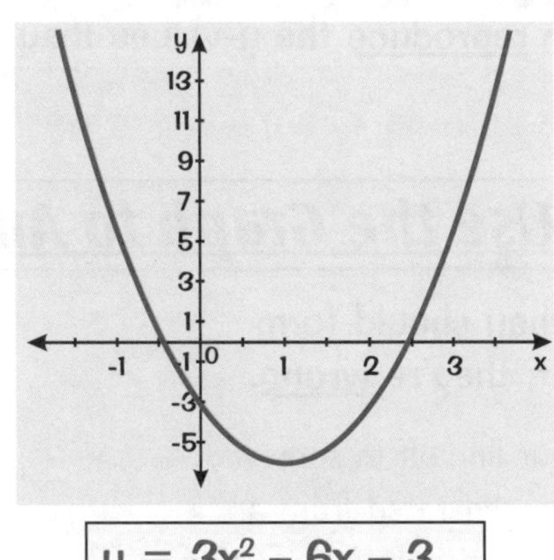

$y = 3x^2 - 6x - 3$

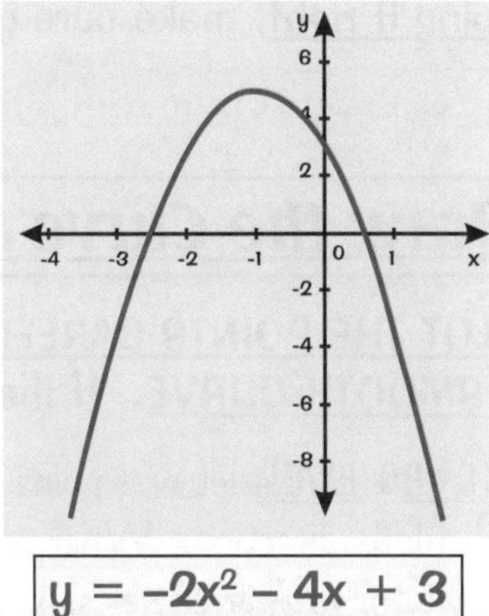

$y = -2x^2 - 4x + 3$

x^3 GRAPHS: $y = ax^3 + bx^2 + cx + d$ (b, c and/or d can be zero)

Equations with an x^3 term in them are called cubic equations. The graphs of these equations always have the same wiggle in the middle and are called cubic graphs.

Sometimes cubic graphs have a flat wiggle, sometimes it's more pronounced.
$-x^3$ graphs always go down from top left, $+x^3$ ones go up from bottom left.

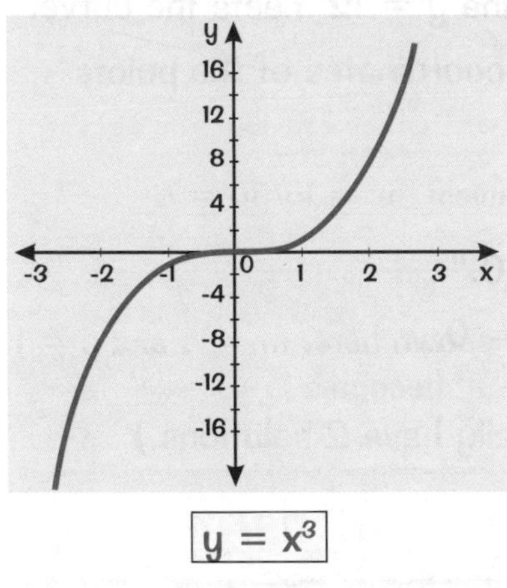

$y = x^3$

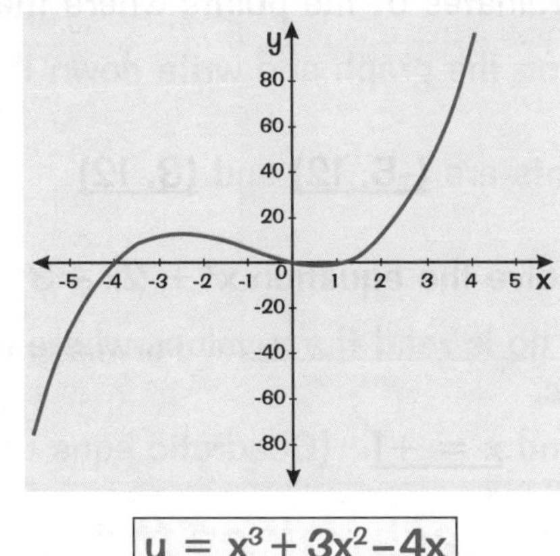

$y = x^3 + 3x^2 - 4x$

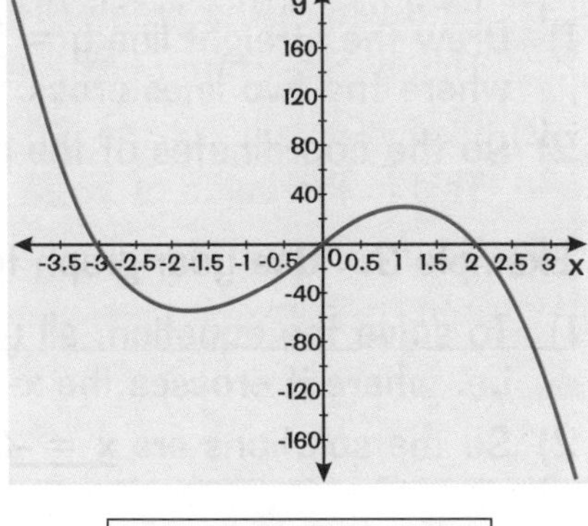

$y = -7x^3 - 7x^2 + 42x$

Quadratics and Cubics — they're a right graph...

Learn the equations and shapes of both types of graph, then turn over and sketch 2 examples of each.

1) Describe the following graphs in words: a) $y = 3x^2 + 2$ b) $y = 4 - x^3$

Quadratic and Cubic Graphs

Sadly for you, simply recognising quadratic and cubic graphs probably won't be enough to get you through the exam. Chances are you'll have to answer some questions on them as well. Luckily, most questions follow a set pattern...

Fill in the Table of Values

Example: "Fill in the table of values for the equation $y = x^2 + 2x - 3$ and draw the graph."

x	-5	-4	-3	-2	-1	0	1	2	3
y		5		-3	-4	-3	0		

Work out each point <u>very carefully</u>, writing down all your working. To check you're <u>doing it right</u>, make sure you can <u>reproduce</u> the y-values they've already given you.

Draw the Curve and Use the Graph to Answer a Question

<u>PLOT THE POINTS CAREFULLY</u>, they should form a <u>SMOOTH CURVE</u>. If they don't, they're <u>wrong</u>.

<u>NEVER EVER</u> let one point drag your line off in some ridiculous direction. When a graph is generated from an equation, <u>you never get spikes or lumps</u> — only <u>MISTAKES</u>.

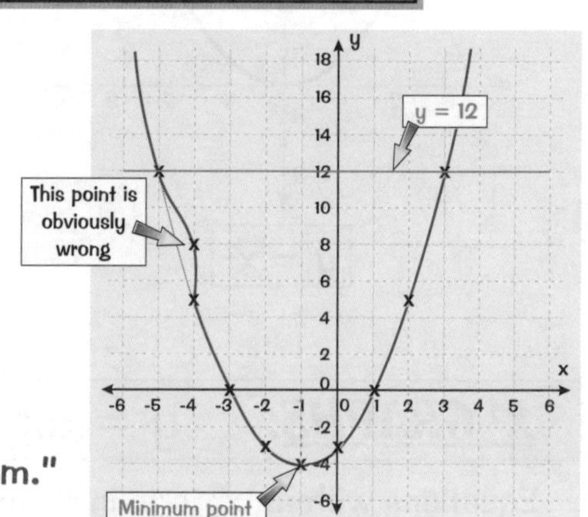

Drawing a graph is often just the <u>first stage</u> of a question, you'll usually have to <u>interpret</u> it as well:

Example 1: "Give the value of x for which $x^2 + 2x - 3$ is a minimum."

1) Find the point on the graph where y is at its lowest value — the minimum point — and read off the corresponding x-value.
2) So the value of x for which $x^2 + 2x - 3$ is a minimum is <u>-1</u>.

Example 2: "Write down the coordinates of the points where the line $y = 12$ meets the curve."

1) Draw the straight line $y = 12$ on the graph and write down the coordinates of the points where the two lines cross.
2) So the coordinates of the points are <u>(-5, 12)</u> and <u>(3, 12)</u>.

Example 3: "Use your graph to solve the equation $x^2 + 2x - 3 = 0$."

1) To solve the equation, all you do is read the x-values where $y = 0$, i.e. where it crosses the x-axis.
2) So the solutions are <u>$x = -3$</u> and <u>$x = +1$</u>. (Quadratic eqns usually have 2 solutions.)

Make sure your graphs are smoother than a polished kipper...

<u>Learn</u> the details of the method above for <u>drawing graphs</u> and <u>interpreting</u> them.
Plot the graph of $y = x^2 - x - 6$ (use x-values from -4 to 5).
Use your graph to solve the equation $x^2 - x - 6 = 0$.

Algebra

Algebra really terrifies so many people. But honestly, it's not that bad. You've just got to make sure you understand and learn these basic rules for dealing with algebraic expressions. After that, all it needs is practice, practice, practice... and a little love.

Letters Multiplied Together

This is the super-slick notation they like to use in algebra which just ends up making life difficult for folks like you. You've got to remember these five rules:

1) 'abc' means '$a \times b \times c$' The ×'s are often left out to make it clearer.

2) 'gn^2' means '$g \times n \times n$' Note that only the n is squared, not the g as well.

3) '$(gn)^2$' means '$g \times g \times n \times n$' The brackets mean that **BOTH** letters are squared.

4) '$p(q - r)^3$' means '$p \times (q - r) \times (q - r) \times (q - r)$' Only the brackets get cubed.

5) '-3^2' is not clear. It should either be written $(-3)^2 = 9$, or $-(3^2) = -9$.

Terms

Before you can do anything else, you **MUST** understand what a **TERM** is:

1) **A TERM IS A COLLECTION OF NUMBERS, LETTERS AND BRACKETS, ALL MULTIPLIED/DIVIDED TOGETHER.**

2) Terms are SEPARATED BY + AND – SIGNS e.g. $4x^2 - 3py - 5 + 3p$ (Terms)

3) Terms always have a + or – ATTACHED TO THE FRONT OF THEM

4) e.g.

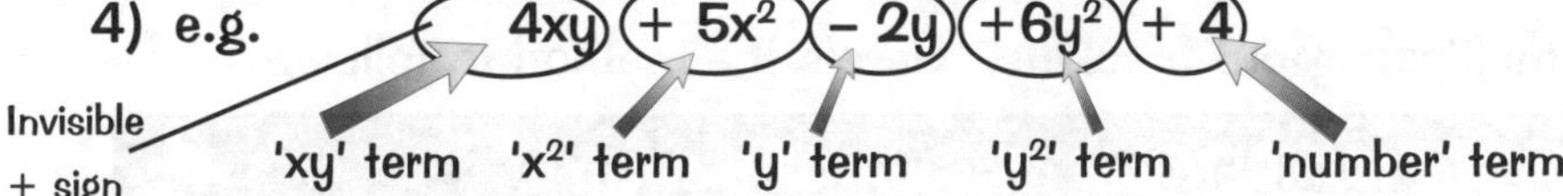

Simplifying

'Collecting Like Terms'

EXAMPLE: "Simplify $2x - 4 + 5x + 6$"

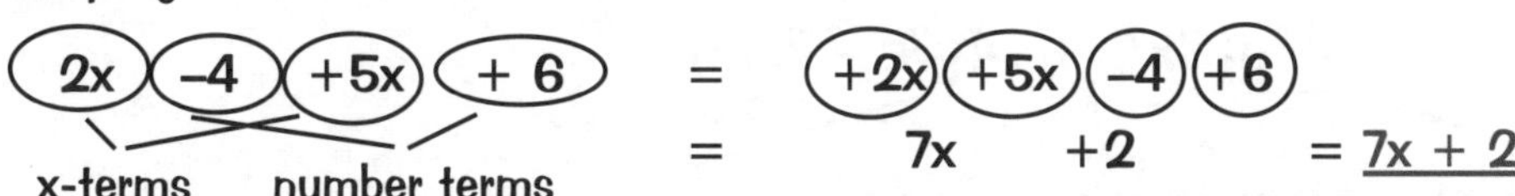

1) Put bubbles round each term, — be sure you capture the +/– sign IN FRONT of each.

2) Then you can move the bubbles into the best order so that LIKE TERMS are together.

3) 'LIKE TERMS' have exactly the same combination of letters, e.g. 'x-terms' or 'xy-terms'.

4) Combine LIKE TERMS using the NUMBER LINE (not the other rule for negative numbers).

Ahhh algebra, it's as easy as abc, or ab^2, or something like that...

Learn all the key facts on this page, then have a go at these questions to see how well you've got it.

1) Simplify: a) $5x + 3y - 4 - 2y - x$ b) $3x + 2 + 5xy + 6x - 7$
c) $2x + 3x^2 + 5y^2 + 3x$ d) $3y - 6xy + 3y + 2yx$

2) If $m=2$ and $n=-3$, work out: a) mn^2 b) $(mn)^3$ c) $m(4+n)^2$ d) n^3 e) $3m^2n^3 + 2mn$

Algebra

More algebra coming your way...

Dealing with Powers

You treat powers in algebra the same way as you'd treat numbers written as powers (see p.50).

EXAMPLES: $x^2 \times x^4 = x^{2+4} = x^6$ $(x^4)^3 = x^{4\times3} = x^{12}$ $x^6 \div x^2 = x^{6-2} = x^4$

If there are numbers and letters involved, you need to work them out separately.

EXAMPLES: $3x^2 \times 2x^4 = (3 \times 2)x^{2+4} = 6x^6$ $(2x^4)^3 = 2^3x^{4\times3} = 8x^{12}$

Multiplying out Brackets

1) The thing OUTSIDE the brackets multiplies each separate term INSIDE the brackets.
2) When letters are multiplied together, they are just written next to each other, e.g. pq
3) Remember, $R \times R = R^2$, and TY^2 means $T\times Y\times Y$, whilst $(TY)^2$ means $T\times T\times Y\times Y$.
4) Remember a minus outside the bracket REVERSES ALL THE SIGNS when you multiply.

EXAMPLE: 1) $3(2x + 5) = 6x + 15$ 2) $4p(3r - 2t) = 12pr - 8pt$

3) $-4(3p^2 - 7q^3) = -12p^2 + 28q^3$ — (note both signs have been reversed — Rule 4)

Factorising — putting brackets in

This is the exact reverse of multiplying-out brackets. Here's the method to follow:

1) Take out the biggest NUMBER that goes into all the terms.
2) For each letter in turn, take out the highest power (e.g. x, x^2 etc) that will go into EVERY term.
3) Open the brackets and fill in all the bits needed to reproduce each term.

EXAMPLE: Factorise $15x^4y + 20x^2y^3z - 35x^3yz^2$

ANSWER: $5x^2y(3x^2 + 4y^2z - 7xz^2)$

Biggest number that'll divide into 15, 20 and 35

Highest powers of x and y that will go into all three terms

z wasn't in ALL terms so it can't come out as a common factor

REMEMBER: 1) The bits taken out and put at the front are the common factors.
2) The bits inside the brackets are what's needed to get back to the original terms if you were to multiply the brackets out again.

Go forth and multiply out brackets...

The techniques on this page are the nuts n' bolts of algebra. There's no getting out of it, you'll have to knuckle down and learn everything on the page inside out. Then have a crack at these:

1) Expand: a) $2(x - 2)$ b) $x(5 + x)$ c) $y(y + x)$ d) $3y(2x - 6)$
2) Factorise: a) $5xy + 15x$ b) $5a - 7ab$ c) $12xy + 6y - 36y^2$

Number Patterns and Sequences

There are five different types of number sequences you could get in the exam, each as pretty as the last. They're not difficult — AS LONG AS YOU WRITE WHAT'S HAPPENING IN EACH GAP.

1) 'Add or Subtract the Same Number'

The SECRET is to write the differences in the gaps between each pair of numbers:

E.g. 2 5 8 11 14 ... (+3 +3 +3 +3 +3)

30 24 18 12 ... (-6 -6 -6 -6)

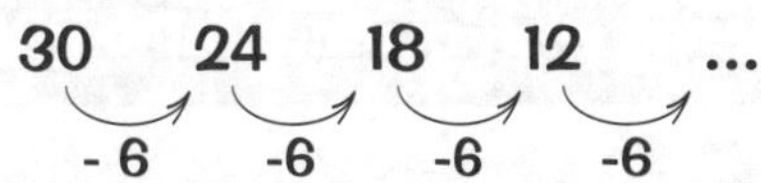

The RULE: 'Add 3 to the previous term' 'Subtract 6 from the previous term'

2) 'Add or Subtract a Changing Number'

Again, WRITE THE CHANGE IN THE GAPS, as shown here:

E.g. 8 11 15 20 26 ... (+3 +4 +5 +6 +7) or 53 43 34 26 19 ... (-10 -9 -8 -7 -6)

The RULE: 'Add 1 extra each time to the previous term' 'Subtract 1 less from the previous term'

3) Multiply by the Same Number each Time

This type have a common MULTIPLIER linking each pair of numbers:

E.g. 5 10 20 40 ... (×2 ×2 ×2 ×2)

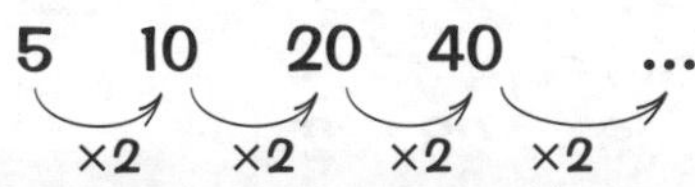

2 6 18 54 ... (×3 ×3 ×3 ×3)

The RULE: 'Multiply the previous term by 2' 'Multiply the previous term by 3'

4) Divide by the Same Number each Time

This type have the same DIVIDER between each pair of numbers:

E.g. 400 200 100 50 ... (÷2 ÷2 ÷2 ÷2)

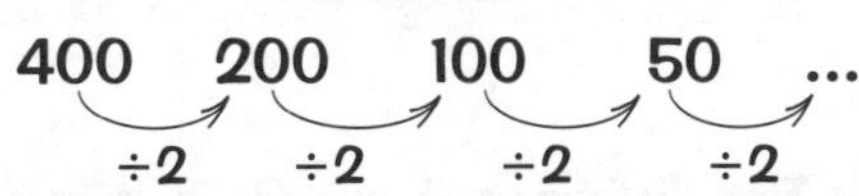

40 000 4000 400 40 ... (÷10 ÷10 ÷10 ÷10)

The RULE: 'Divide the previous term by 2' 'Divide the previous term by 10'

5) Add the Previous Two Terms

This type of sequence works by adding the last two numbers to get the next one.

E.g. 1 1 2 3 5 8 13 ... (1+1 1+2 2+3 3+5 5+8 8+13)

2 4 6 10 16 ... (2+4 4+6 6+10 10+16)

The RULE: 'Add the previous two terms'

Number Patterns and Sequences

'State the rule for extending the pattern'

This is what a lot of Exam questions end up asking for and it's easy enough so long as you remember this:

ALWAYS say what you do to the PREVIOUS TERM to get the next term.

All the number sequences on the previous page have the rule for extending the pattern written in the box underneath them. Notice that they all refer to the previous term.

Finding the nth number:

You could be asked in the Exam to 'give an expression for the nth number in the sequence.' You'll only have to do this for a 'type 1' sequence (where the same number is added or subtracted). It's not that difficult because there's a simple formula:

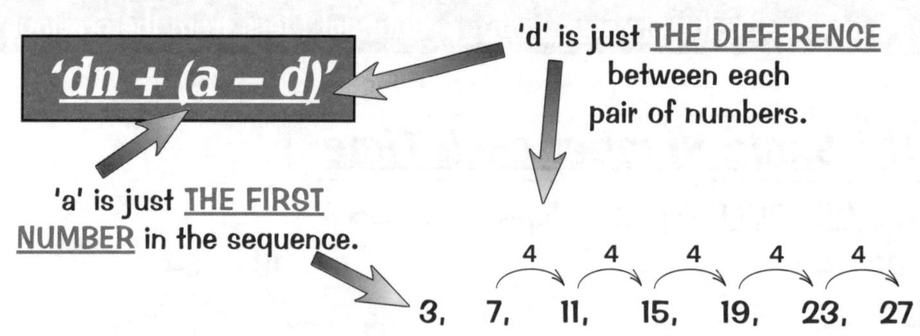

To get the nth term, you just find the values of 'a' and 'd' from the sequence and stick them in the formula. You don't replace n though — that wants to stay as n. Of course you have to learn the formula, but life is like that.

Example: "Find the nth number of this sequence: 5, 8, 11, 14 ...."

1) The formula is $dn + (a - d)$
2) The first number is 5, so $a = 5$. The differences are 3 so $d = 3$
3) Putting these in the formula gives: $3n + (5 - 3) = 3n + 2$

So the nth number for this sequence is given by: '$3n + 2$'

Look, if I've told you n times, I've told you n + 1 times — learn this page...

LEARN the 5 types of number patterns and the formula for finding the nth number and Bob's your uncle.

1) Find the next two numbers in each of these sequences, and say in words what the rule is:

a) 2, 5, 9, 14 .... b) 2, 20, 200 .... c) 64, 32, 16, 8 ...

2) Find the expression for the nth number in this sequence: 7, 9, 11, 13

Solving Equations

The 'proper' way to solve equations is on the next page, but there are some easier methods shown below. You can't use them on complicated equations, but most of the time they do just fine.

Forming Equations

Forming equations is easy — you just substitute letters in for any numbers that you don't know.

Example: Jenny is given £5 pocket money. She spends £x at the school tuck shop and has £y left. Write an equation to represent this.

Answer: Jenny started off with £5 and she spent £x, so she must have $5 - x$ pounds left. So $y = 5 - x$.

Solving Equations — The 'Common Sense' Approach

The trick here is to realise that the unknown quantity 'x' is after all just a number and the 'equation' is just a cryptic clue to help you find it

Example: "Solve this equation: $3x + 4 = 46$"
(i.e. find what number x is)

Answer: This is what you should say to yourself:

"Something + 4 = 46" hmm, so that 'something' must be 42.

So that means $3x = 42$, which means '3 times something = 42'

So it must be $42 \div 3$ which is 14 so $x = 14$

In other words don't think of it as algebra, but as 'Find the mystery number'.

Solving Equations — The Trial and Error Method

This is a perfectly good method, and although it won't work every time, it usually does, especially if the answer is a whole number.

The big secret of trial and error methods is to find TWO OPPOSITE CASES and keep taking values IN BETWEEN them.

In other words, find a number that makes the Right Hand Side bigger, and then one that makes the Left Hand Side bigger, and then try values in between them.

Example: "Solve for x: $3x + 5 = 21 - 5x$"
(i.e. find the number x)

Answer:

Try x=1: $3 + 5 = 21 - 5$, $8 = 16$ — no good, RHS too big

Try x=3: $9 + 5 = 21 - 15$, $14 = 6$ — no good, now LHS too big

SO TRY IN BETWEEN: $x = 2$: $6 + 5 = 21 - 10$, $11 = 11$, YES, so $x = 2$.

But I'm innocent your honour — this trial is an error...

~~Loan those two methods~~. No. ~~Learn these to meatheads~~. No. Learn these two methods. Splendid.

1) Solve: $4x - 12 = 20$
2) Solve: $3x + 5 = 5x - 9$

Solving Equations

The 'proper' way of solving equations isn't hard, it just needs lots of practice.

Solving Equations — The 'Proper' Way

Golden Rules

1) Always do the SAME thing to both sides of the equation.
2) To get rid of something, do the opposite.
   The opposite of + is – and the opposite of – is +.
   The opposite of × is ÷ and the opposite of ÷ is ×.
3) Keep going until you have a letter on its own.

Example 1: Solve $5x = 15$

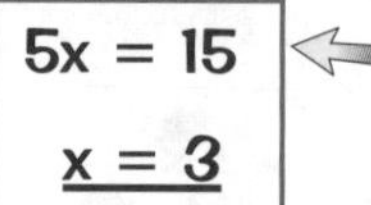

$5x = 15$

$\underline{x = 3}$

5x means 5 × x, so do the opposite — divide both sides by 5.

Example 2: Solve $\frac{p}{3} = 2$

$\frac{p}{3} = 2$

$\underline{p = 6}$

$\frac{p}{3}$ means p ÷ 3, so do the opposite — multiply both sides by 3.

Example 3: Solve $4y - 3 = 17$

$4y - 3 = 17$ — The opposite of –3 is +3 so add 3 to both sides.

$4y = 20$ — The opposite of ×4 is ÷4 so divide both sides by 4.

$\underline{y = 5}$

Example 4: Solve $2(x + 3) = 11$

$2(x + 3) = 11$ — The opposite of ×2 is ÷2 so divide both sides by 2.

$x + 3 = 5.5$ — The opposite of +3 is –3 so subtract 3 from both sides.

$\underline{x = 2.5}$

Example 5: Solve $3x + 5 = 5x + 1$

there are x's on both sides, so subtract 3x from both sides. → $3x + 5 = 5x + 1$

the opposite of +1 is –1, so subtract 1 from each side. → $5 = 2x + 1$

the opposite of ×2 is ÷2, so divide each side by 2. → $4 = 2x$

$\underline{2 = x}$

Rearranging Formulas

You do this in exactly the same way that you solve equations — watch...

Example 6: Rearrange the formula $q = 3p + 4$ to make p the subject:

$q = 3p + 4$

The opposite of +4 is –4 so take 4 from both sides. → $q - 4 = 3p$

The opposite of ×3 is ÷3 so divide both sides by 3. → $\frac{q - 4}{3} = p$

Dear Jim — could you fix it for me to make P the subject of this formula...

It's always good to know the proper way to solve equations, just in case you get thrown a curveball in the exam and they give you a real nightmare of an equation to solve.

1) Solve these equations: a) $3x + 1 = 13$ b) $q/_4 = 8$ c) $5y + 4 = 2y - 2$
2) Rearrange this formula to make b the subject: $2(b - 3) = a$

Inequalities

I'm not going to lie to you, some of this is a bit nasty. But I reckon you're up to it...

The 4 Inequality Symbols:

$>$ means '<u>Greater than</u>' $\geq$ means '<u>Greater than or equal to</u>'

$<$ means '<u>Less than</u>' $\leq$ means '<u>Less than or equal to</u>'

<u>REMEMBER</u>, the one at the <u>BIG</u> end is <u>BIGGEST</u>

so '$x > 4$' and '$4 < x$' <u>BOTH</u> say: '<u>x is greater than 4</u>'

Algebra With Inequalities — this is generally a bit tricky

The thing to remember here is that <u>inequalities are just like regular equations</u>:

$5x < x + 2$

$5x = x + 2$

in the sense that <u>all the normal rules for solving equations</u> (See P.68) <u>apply</u>...

...<u>BUT WITH ONE BIG EXCEPTION</u>:

Whenever you MULTIPLY OR DIVIDE BY A <u>NEGATIVE NUMBER</u>, you must <u>FLIP THE INEQUALITY SIGN</u>.

Example: "<u>Solve $5x < 6x + 2$</u>"

Answer: Subtract 6x from both sides: $5x - 6x < 2$

combining the x-terms gives: $-x < 2$

To get rid of the '–' in front of x you need to <u>divide both sides by -1</u> — but remember that means the '$<$' has to be flipped as well, which gives:

<u>$x > -2$</u> i.e. '<u>x is greater than -2</u>' is the answer

(The $<$ has flipped around into a $>$, because we divided by a –ve number)

This answer, <u>$x > -2$</u>, can be displayed on a number line like this:

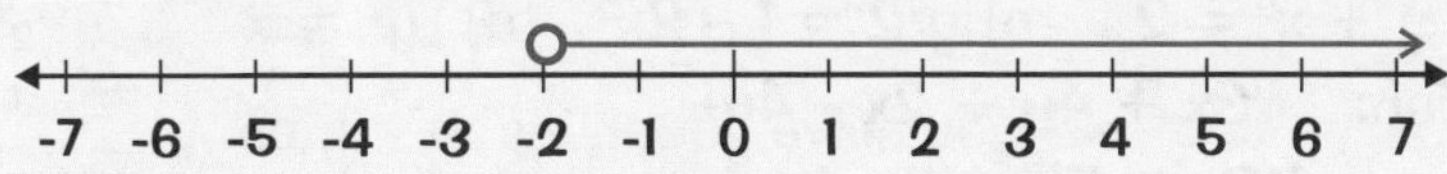

The main thing you should realise, is that <u>MOST OF THE TIME</u> you just treat the '$<$' or '$>$' as though it was an '=' and <u>do all the usual algebra</u> that you would for a regular equation. The '<u>Big Exception</u>' doesn't actually come up very often at all.

Algebra with inequalities? Go and wash your mouth out young man...

Yikes, I'm glad that's over. Right, learn: The <u>4 Inequality Signs</u>, the <u>similarity</u> with <u>equations</u> and the <u>One Big Exception</u>. And then have a crack at these beautiful questions:

1) Solve this inequality: $4x + 3 \leqslant 6x + 7$.
2) Solve the inequalities and find the integer values of x which satisfy both:
   $2x + 9 \geqslant 1$ and $4x < 6 + x$

Revision Summary for Unit Two — 1

WHAT YOU'RE SUPPOSED TO DO HERE is put all the methods covered in Unit Two so far into practice to answer these questions.

1) Jan needs to buy 100 large envelopes at £1.20 each. How much money does she need?
2) Chris bought 100 chocolate bars for £32 to sell in the school tuck shop. How much should he sell each chocolate bar for to make his money back?
3) It cost Asik £150 to print 300 programmes for the School play. How much should he sell each programme for to make his money back?
4) Use written methods to work out: a) £5.55 + 50p + £1.11 b) 8.53 – 2.66.
5) Use written methods to work out: a) 7×32 b) $162 \div 3$
6) What are cube numbers? Write down the first ten of them.
7) Find all the prime numbers between 40 and 60 (there are 5 of them).
8) What are Multiples? Find the first six multiples of 10 and also of 4.
9) Express as a product of prime factors: a) 210 b) 1050
10) Find the least common multiple of 8 and 10.
11) Work out the value of: a) 6^4 b) 4 squared
12) Find all possible answers of a) $\sqrt{256}$ b) $\sqrt[3]{216}$.
13) Convert 0.645 into a fraction.
14) Work out: a) $\frac{4}{6} \times 4\frac{2}{5}$ b) $\frac{25}{6} \div \frac{8}{3}$ c) $\frac{5}{8} + \frac{9}{4}$ d) $\frac{2}{3} - \frac{1}{7}$
15) Estimate the answer to $\frac{390}{28 + 12.3}$
16) Claire and James are playing battleships. Their grids, with their ships shown in grey, are drawn on the right.
    a) Claire guesses the point (7, 2) on James's grid. James says "miss". Is he cheating?
    b) James guesses (4, 6) on Claire's grid. Has he hit a ship?

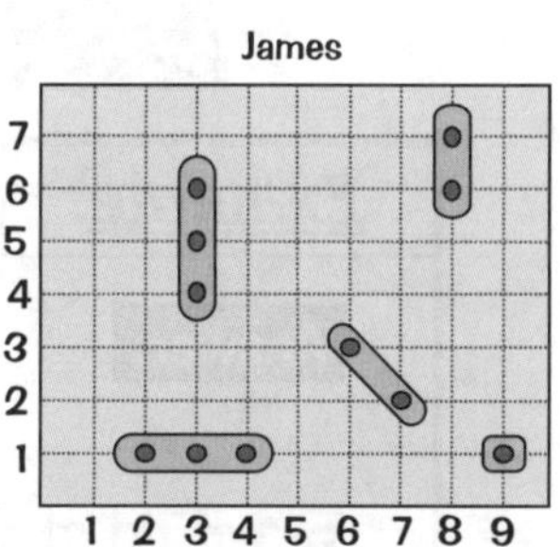

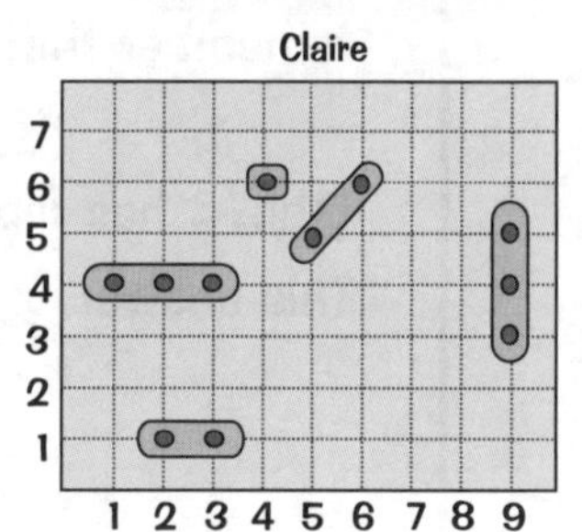

17) a) Complete the table of values below for the equation: $y = x + 3$
    b) Draw the graph.

x	-5	-3	-1	0	1	2	4	6
y	-2				4			

18) Say if each of the following are straight line equations or quadratics.
    a) $x + 3 = y$ b) $y + x^2 = 2$ c) $y/2 = 1 - 2x$ d) $y^2 = x$
19) Simplify the expression: $3x + 4y + 2x - 4y$
20) Expand this expression: $4(3g + 5h - 1)$
21) Factorise (take out common factors) this expression: $2x + 6xy$.
22) Find the next two terms in these sequences of numbers:
    a) 3, 7, 11, 15, ... b) 36, 28, 21, 15, 10, ...
    For each sequence, say what the rule is for extending the pattern.
23) Work out the expression for the nth number in this sequence: 1, 5, 9, 13, ...
24) 'To find y you double x and add 4.' Write this as a formula.
25) For each of these, make y the subject:
    a) $6 - y = x$ b) $11 + 2y = x$ c) $y/3 = 7x + 3$
26) Solve these inequalities:
    a) $5x < 25$ b) $20 - 5x > 25$ c) $-6x < 30$ d) $10x > 170 - 7x$

Symmetry

Symmetry is where a shape or picture can be put in different positions that look exactly the same. There are THREE types of symmetry, and guess what — you need to know about them all.

1) Line Symmetry

This is where you can draw a MIRROR LINE (or more than one) across a picture and both sides will fold exactly together.

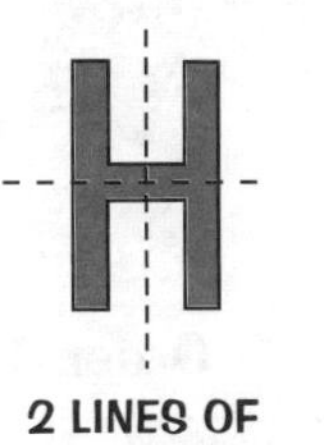

2 LINES OF SYMMETRY

1 LINE OF SYMMETRY

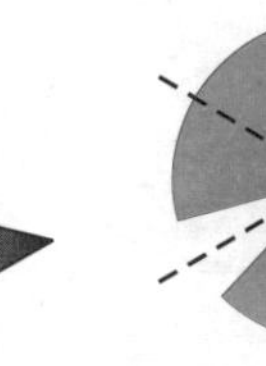

1 LINE OF SYMMETRY

3 LINES OF SYMMETRY

NO LINES OF SYMMETRY

1 LINE OF SYMMETRY

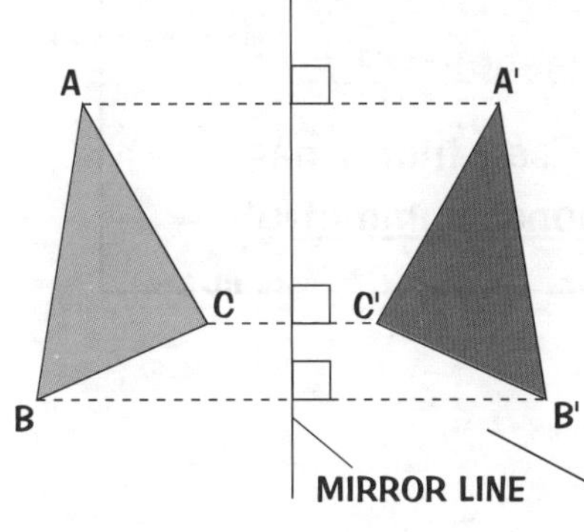

How to Draw a Reflection:

1) Reflect each point one by one.
2) Use a line which crosses the mirror line at 90° and goes EXACTLY the same distance on the other side of the mirror line, as shown.
3) Reflected shapes are congruent (see p.97) — they're the same size and shape as each other.

A line which crosses at 90° is called a perpendicular

2) Plane Symmetry

Plane Symmetry is all to do with 3-D SOLIDS. Just like flat shapes can have a mirror line, so solid 3-D objects can have a plane of symmetry.

A plane mirror surface can be drawn through, but the shape must be exactly the same on both sides of the plane (i.e. mirror images), like these are:

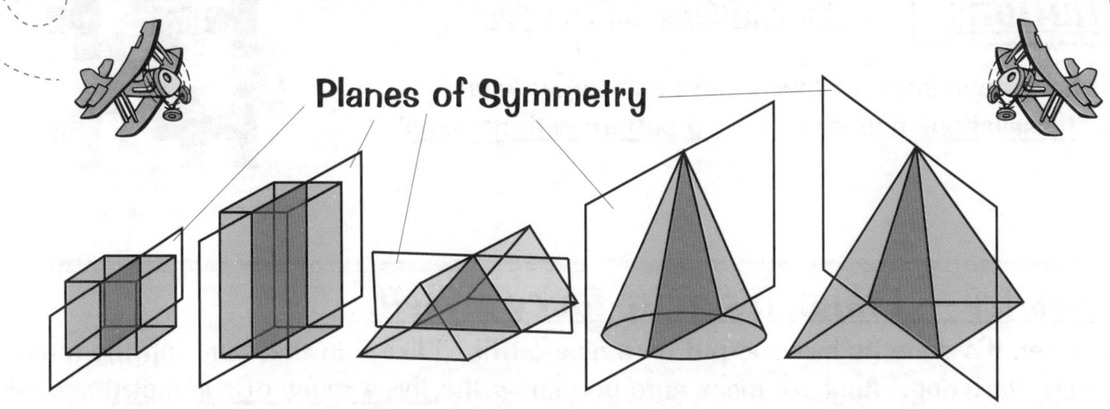

The shapes drawn here all have MANY MORE PLANES OF SYMMETRY but there's only one plane of symmetry drawn in for each shape, because otherwise it would all get really messy and you wouldn't be able to see anything.

Symmetry

3) Rotational Symmetry

This is where you can ROTATE the shape or drawing into different positions that all look exactly the same.

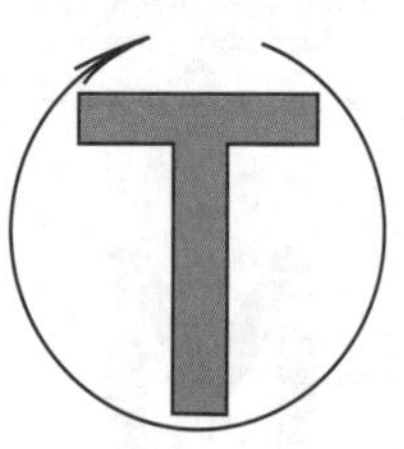

Order 1

Order 2

Order 2

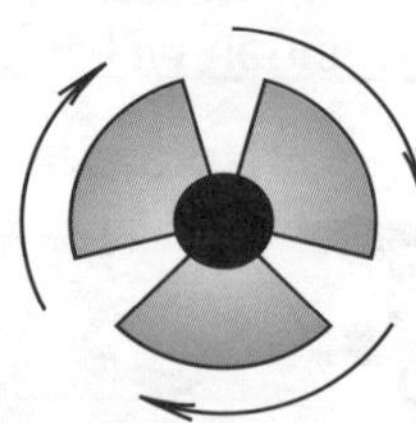

Order 3

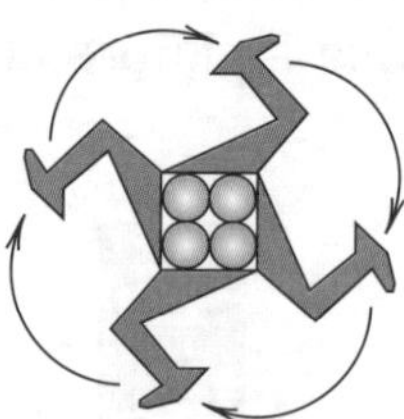

Order 4

The ORDER OF ROTATIONAL SYMMETRY is the posh way of saying: 'HOW MANY DIFFERENT POSITIONS LOOK THE SAME'.
E.g. You should say the Z shape above has 'Rotational Symmetry order 2'

BUT... when a shape has ONLY 1 POSITION you can either say that it has 'Rotational Symmetry order 1' or that it has 'NO Rotational Symmetry'

Tracing Paper

— this always makes symmetry a lot easier

1) For REFLECTIONS, trace one side of the drawing and the mirror line too. Then turn the paper over and line up the mirror line in its original position.
2) For ROTATIONS, just swizzle the paper round. It's really good for finding the centre of rotation (by trial and error) as well as the order of rotational symmetry.
3) You can use tracing paper in the EXAM — ask for it.

Tessellations

— 'Tiling patterns with no gaps'

You must have done loads of these, but don't forget what the name 'tessellation' means — 'a tiling pattern with no gaps':

Plane symmetry — I think it's quite fancy myself...

...you know, when it's done its hair and put on a nice outfit. I like it in that blue top the most — the colour's very flattering. Anyhoo, make sure you know the three types of symmetry and what tessellations are. Then copy the letters below and mark in all the lines of symmetry. Also say what the rotational symmetry is for each one.

H Z T N E X S

The Shapes you Need to Know

These are easy marks in the Exam — make sure you know them all.

Three-sided Shapes — Triangles

(just in case you didn't know...)

1) RIGHT-ANGLED Triangle

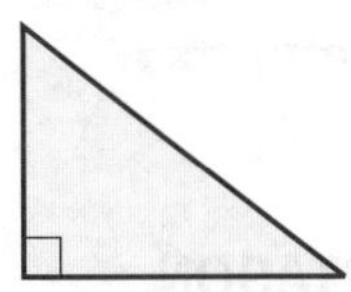

No symmetry unless the angles are 45°

2) SCALENE Triangle

No sides equal
No angles equal

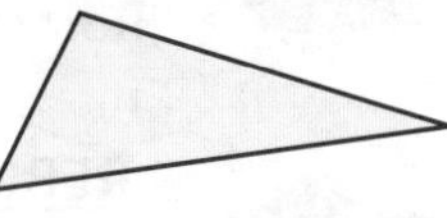

No symmetry

3) ISOSCELES Triangle

2 sides equal
2 angles equal

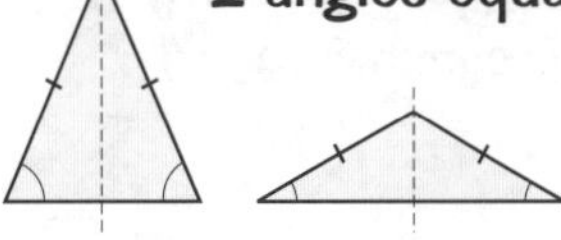

1 line of symmetry.
No rotational symmetry

4) EQUILATERAL Triangle

All sides equal
All angles 60°

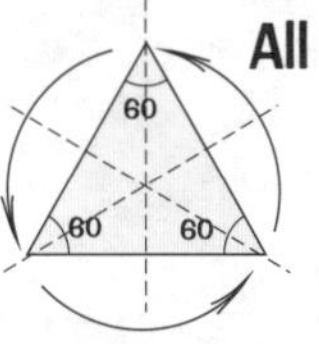

3 lines of symmetry.
Rot^{nl} symm. order 3

Four-sided Shapes — Quadrilaterals

1) SQUARE

4 lines of symmetry.
Rotational symmetry order 4.

2) RECTANGLE

2 lines of symmetry.
Rotational symmetry order 2.

3) RHOMBUS (A square pushed over)
(It's also a diamond)

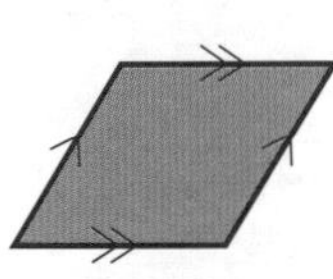

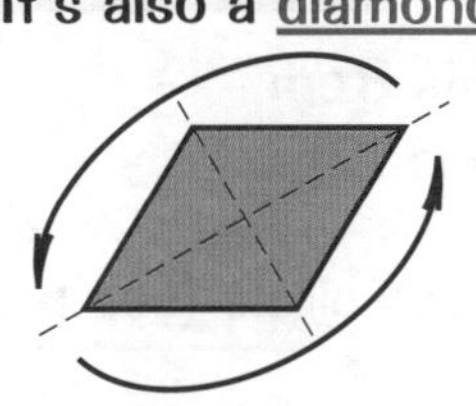

2 lines of symmetry.
Rotational symmetry order 2.

4) PARALLELOGRAM

(A rectangle pushed over — two pairs of parallel sides — see p.79)

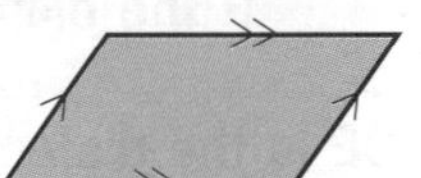

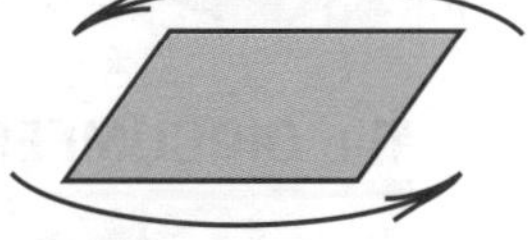

NO lines of symmetry.
Rotational symmetry order 2.

5) TRAPEZIUM (One pair of parallel sides)

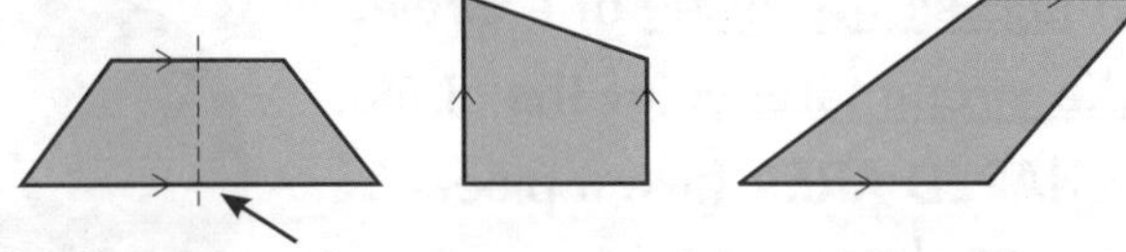

Only the isosceles trapezium has a line of symmetry.
None have rotational symmetry.

6) KITE

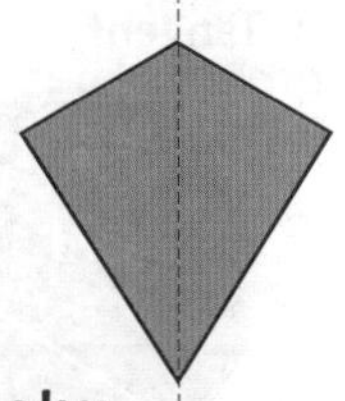

1 line of symmetry.
No rotational symmetry.

Rhombus facts: 4 sides, 2 lines of symmetry, Gemini, peanut allergy...

Learn everything on this page. Then turn over and write down all the details that you can remember. Then try again. It's as simple as that. Then you can play with the kite. Indoors though — it's new.

The Shapes you Need to Know

A polygon is a many-sided shape. A regular polygon is one where all the sides and angles are the same. The regular polygons are a never-ending series of shapes with some fancy features.

You Need to Know These Polygons...

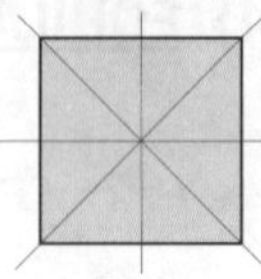

SQUARE
4 sides
4 lines of symmetry
Rot^{nl} symm. order 4

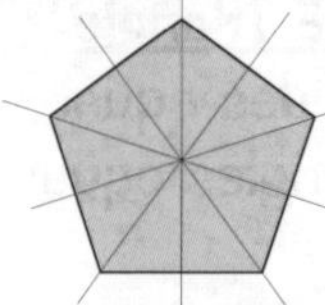

REGULAR PENTAGON
5 sides
5 lines of symmetry
Rot^{nl} symm. order 5

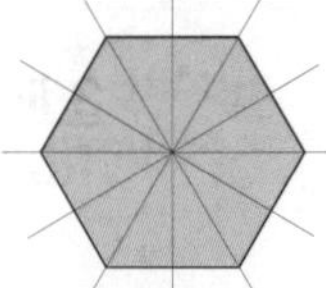

REGULAR HEXAGON
6 sides
6 lines of symmetry
Rot^{nl} symm. order 6

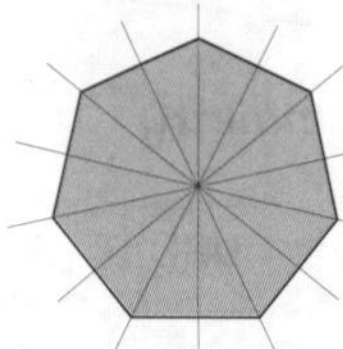

REGULAR HEPTAGON
7 sides
7 lines of symmetry
Rot^{nl} symm. order 7
(A 50p piece is like a heptagon)

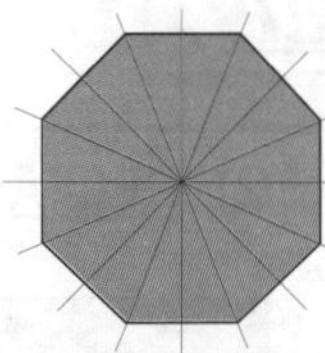

REGULAR OCTAGON
8 sides
8 lines of symmetry
Rot^{nl} symm. order 8

...and These Facts About Circles

1) Radius, Diameter and Circumference

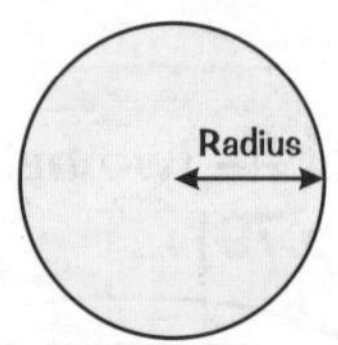

The DIAMETER goes right across the circle.
The RADIUS only goes halfway across.
Examples: If the radius is 4 cm, the diameter is 8 cm,
If the diameter is 24 m, the radius is 12 m.

Remember: the DIAMETER IS EXACTLY DOUBLE THE RADIUS

The CIRCUMFERENCE is the distance round the outside of the circle (see p.27).

2) Tangents, Chords, Arcs and Sectors

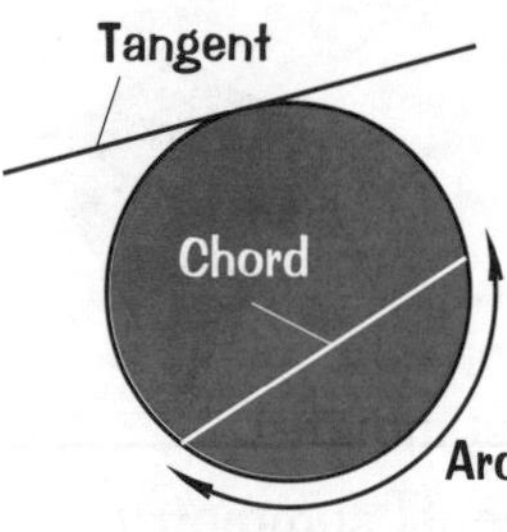

A TANGENT is a straight line that just touches the outside of the circle.
A CHORD is a line drawn across the inside of a circle.
AN ARC is just part of the circumference of the circle.
A SECTOR is a WEDGE SHAPED AREA (like a piece of cake) cut right from the centre.

Minor Arc
Minor Sector
Major Sector
Major Arc

Common mistake — a slice of pie is not called a wedgie...

Once again, learn it all, turn over and scribble it down. If you can remember it all, reward yourself with a pie of your choice. Do I want a wedgie? Oh, well, if you're offering it's rude not to...

3D Shapes and Projections

I was going to make some pop-out 3D shapes to put on this page, but I couldn't find the scissors and sticky tape. Sorry. Still, you need to learn it all though — so chin up and learn the page.

Eight Solids To Learn

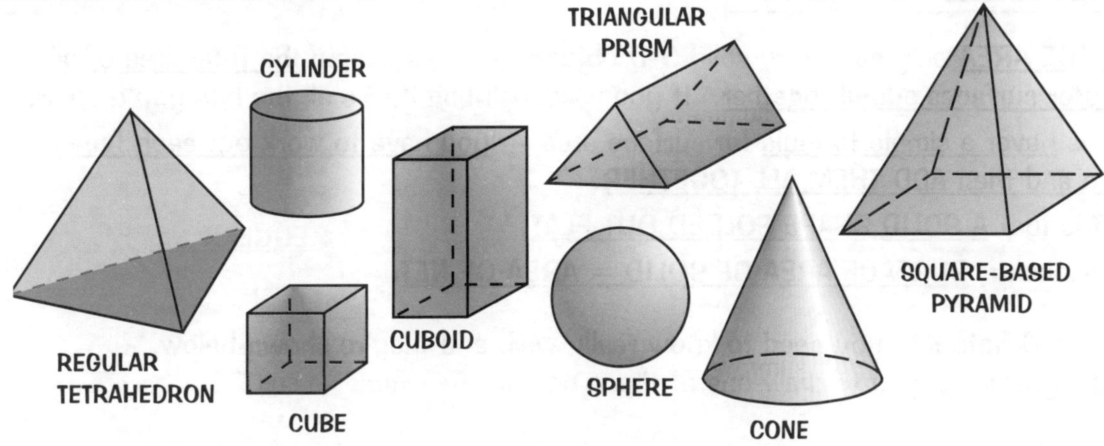

Projections show Different Views of a Shape

A 'projection' shows the relative size and shape of an object from either the front, side or back — they're usually known as 'elevations'. A 'plan' shows the view from above. They're always drawn to scale.
Take this church (naff picture, I know) — you can represent it like this:

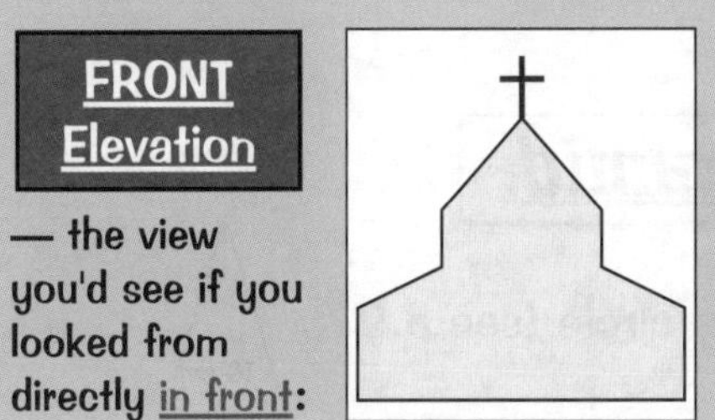

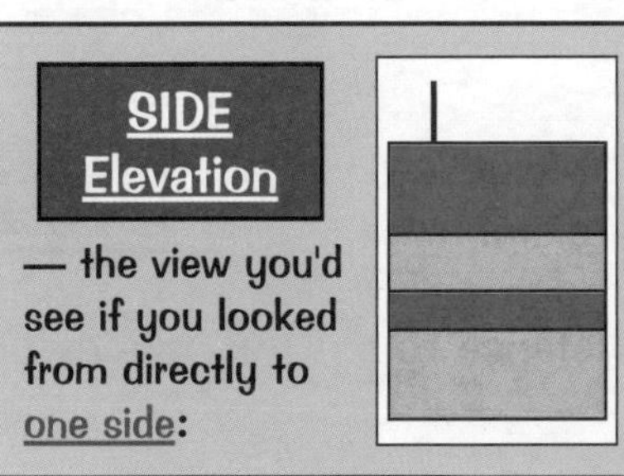

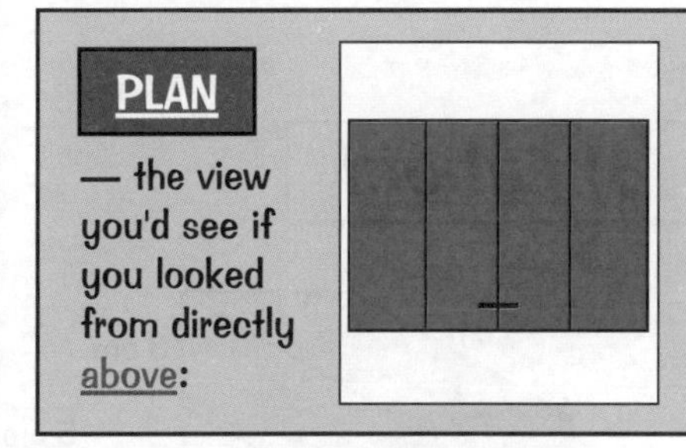

If they're feeling really mean (and they often are), you might get a question on:

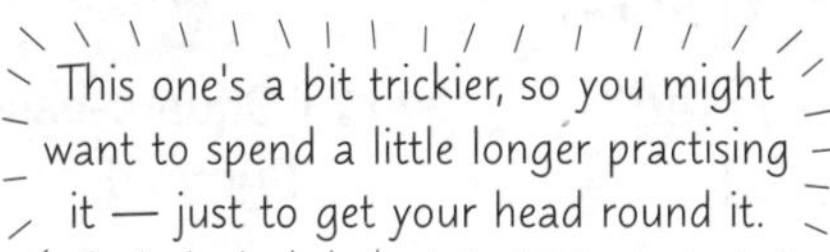

ISOMETRIC Projection

— this is where the shape is drawn (again, to scale) from a view at equal angles to all three axes (x, y and z).
Or more simply, it's a drawing like this:

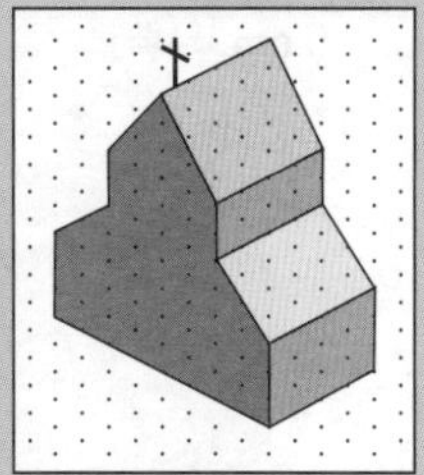

Well done — you've moved on to solids...

Deep breath in... and out... then learn the eight 3D shapes and the four types of projection.
Cover up the page, then name 8 types of solid object.

1) Draw a plan, front and side elevations and an isometric projection of your own house.

Solids and Nets

You need to know what face, edge and vertex mean, and you've come to the right place to find out...

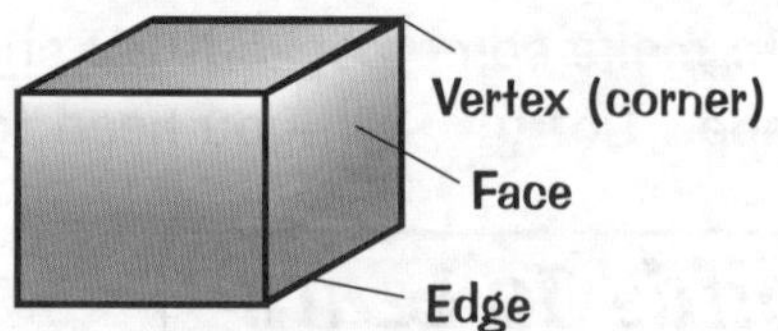

Surface Area and Nets

1) SURFACE AREA only applies to solid 3-D objects, and it's simply the total area of all the outer surfaces added together. If you were painting it, it's all the bits you'd paint.
2) There is never a simple formula for surface area — you have to work out each face in turn and then ADD THEM ALL TOGETHER.
3) A NET is just A SOLID SHAPE FOLDED OUT FLAT.
4) So obviously: SURFACE AREA OF SOLID = AREA OF NET.

There are 4 nets that you need to know really well, and they're shown below. They may well ask you to draw one of these nets in the exam.

1) Triangular Prism

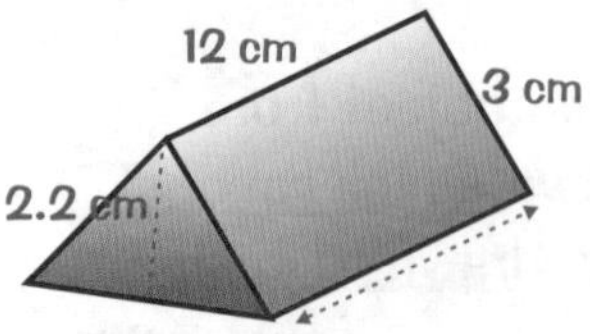

12 cm 3 cm 2.2 cm

Triangular Prism

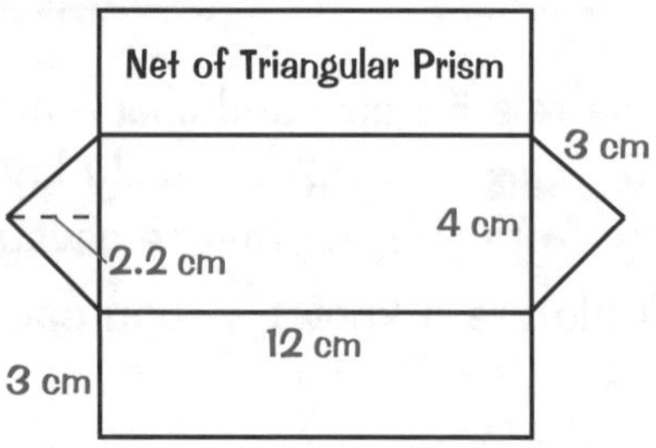

Net of Triangular Prism

3 cm 4 cm 2.2 cm 12 cm 3 cm

2) Cube

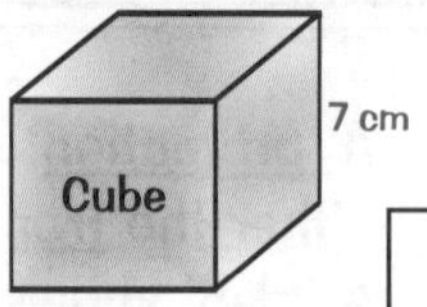

Cube 7 cm

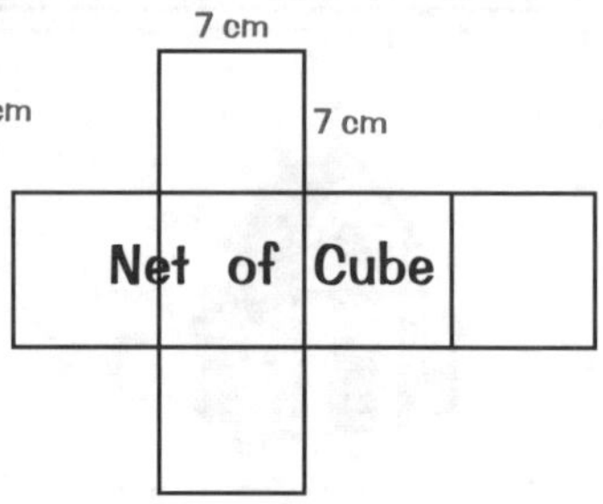

7 cm 7 cm Net of Cube

3) Cuboid

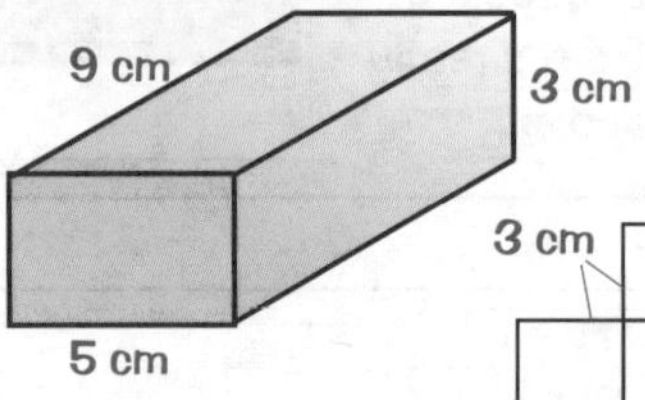

9 cm 3 cm 5 cm

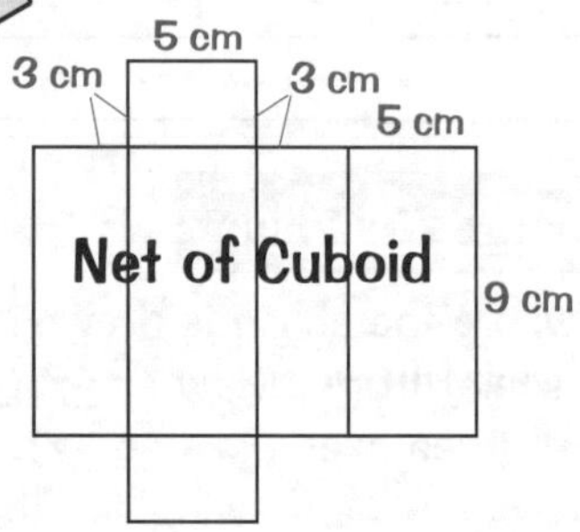

5 cm 3 cm 3 cm 5 cm 9 cm Net of Cuboid

4) Pyramid

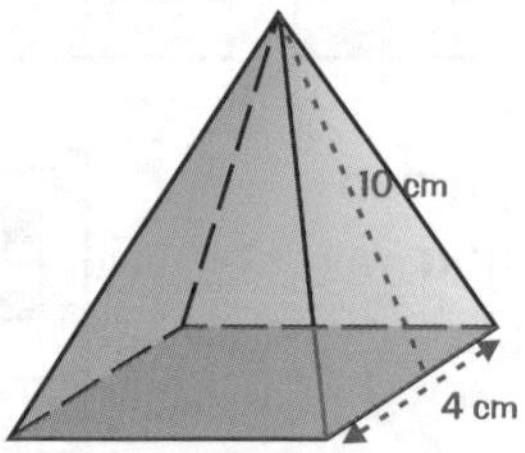

10 cm 4 cm

Square-based Pyramid

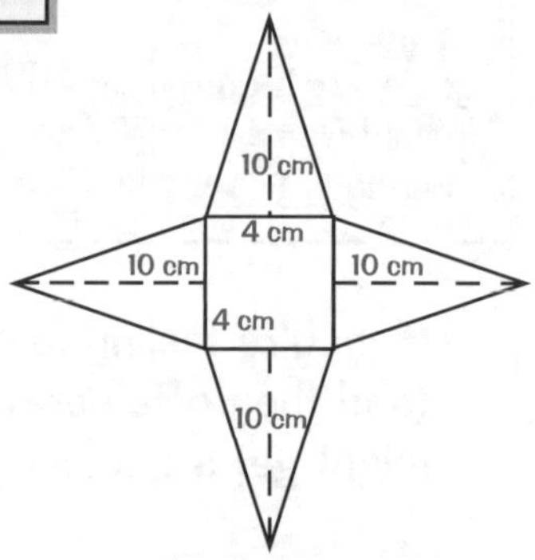

10 cm 4 cm 10 cm 10 cm 4 cm 10 cm

Net of Square-based Pyramid

Edge and vertex, face and toes, face and toes. Edge and vertex....

...face and toes, face and toes. And eyes and ears and mouth and nose. Edge and vertex, face and toes. Face and toes. I didn't make that version up — my nursery was just lame. Make sure you know the four nets above, and memorise the top diagram as well.

Lines and Angles

Angles aren't that bad — you just have to learn them, that's all. And sometimes give them sweets.

Estimating Angles

The secret here is to KNOW THESE FOUR SPECIAL ANGLES as reference points.
Then you can COMPARE any other angle to them.

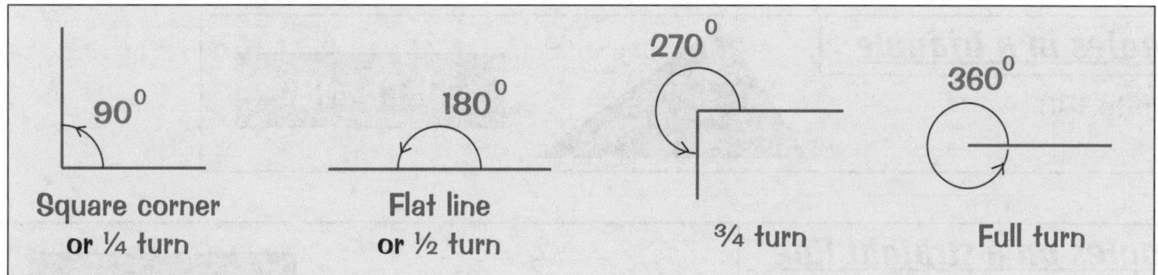

When two lines meet at 90° they are said to be PERPENDICULAR to each other.

EXAMPLE: Estimate the size of these three angles A, B and C:

If you compare each angle to the reference angles of 90°, 180° and 270° you can easily estimate that:

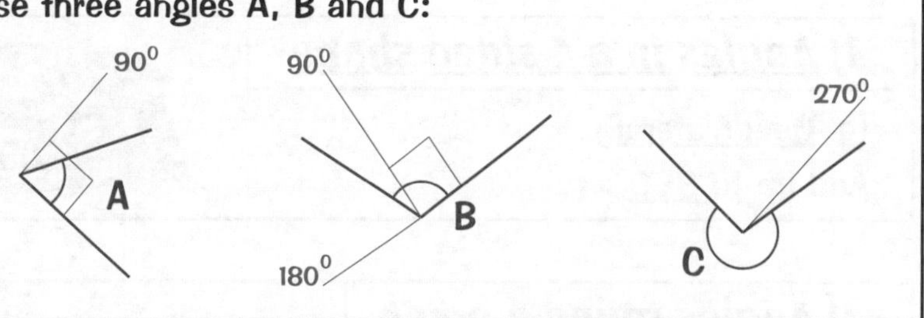

$A \approx 70°$, $B \approx 110°$, $C \approx 260°$

The best way to say which angle you're talking about in a diagram is by using THREE letters. The MIDDLE LETTER is where the angle is, the OTHER TWO LETTERS tell you WHICH TWO LINES enclose the angle. For example in the diagram, angle BCD = 25°.

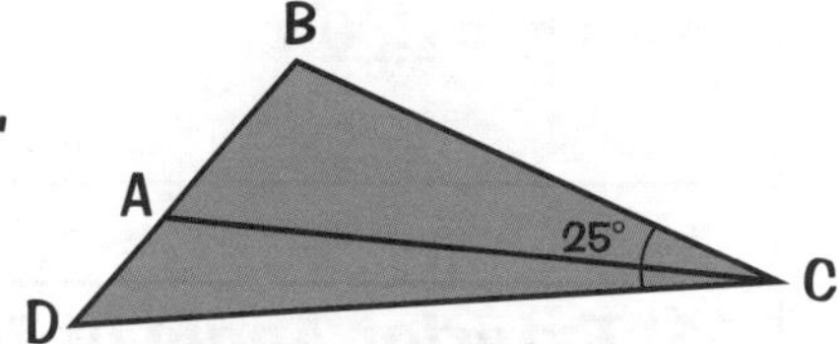

Acute Angles

SHARP POINTY ONES
(less than 90°)

Obtuse Angles

FLATTER-LOOKING ONES
(between 90° and 180°)

Reflex Angles

ONES THAT BEND BACK ON THEMSELVES
(more than 180°)

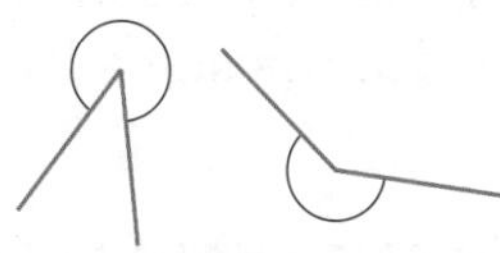

Right Angles

SQUARE CORNERS
(exactly 90°)

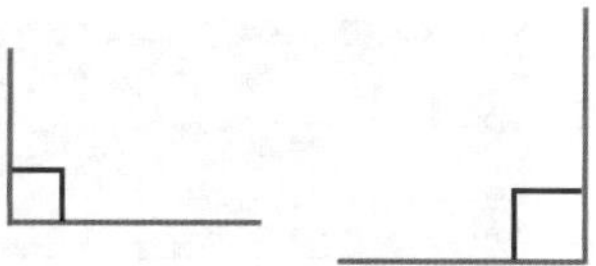

Roses are red, tulips are plum, if you were an angle you'd be acute one...

Ho, ho, ho — pretty funny aren't I. Anyway, moving on...

1) Estimate these angles:

a) 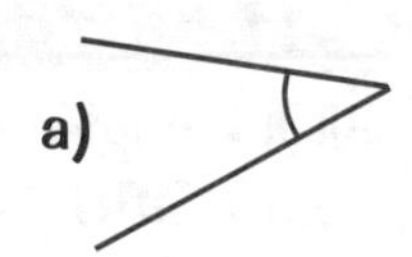

b) 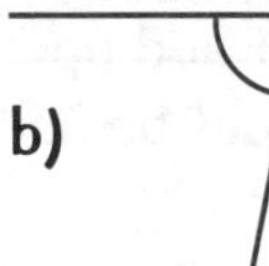

c) 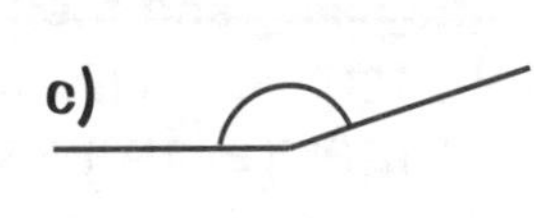

d) 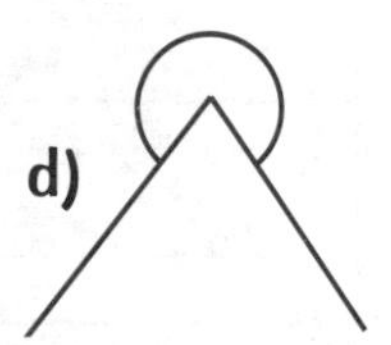

Six Angle Rules

Rules, rules, rules. Gotta love 'em. And even if you don't, you gotta learn 'em. Try these for size:

6 Simple Rules — that's all:

If you know them ALL — THOROUGHLY, you at least have a fighting chance of working out problems with lines and angles. If you don't — you've no chance.

1) Angles in a triangle

Add up to 180°.

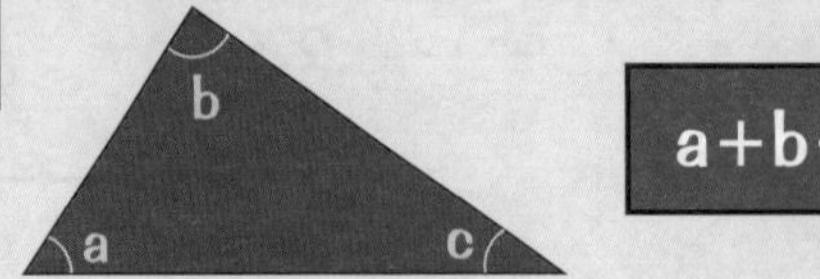

a+b+c=180°

2) Angles on a straight line

Add up to 180°.

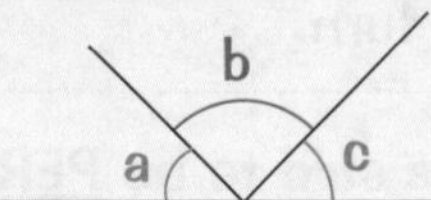

a+b+c=180°

3) Angles in a 4-sided shape

(a 'Quadrilateral')
Add up to 360°.

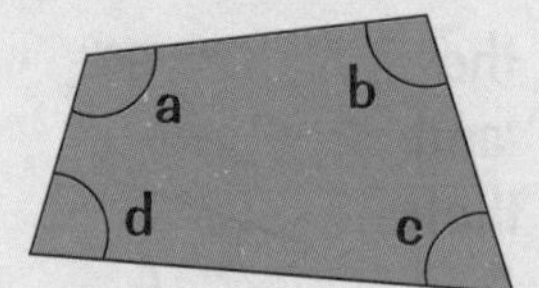

a+b+c+d=360°

4) Angles round a point

Add up to 360°.

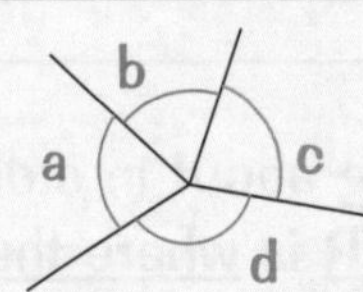

a+b+c+d=360°

5) Exterior Angle of Triangle

Exterior Angle of triangle = sum of Opposite Interior angles

i.e. a+b=d

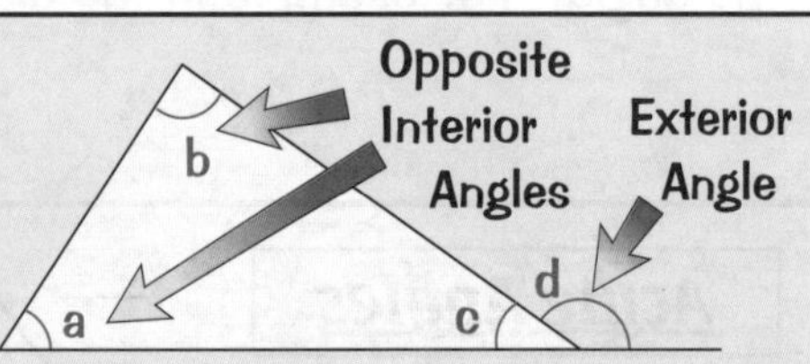

6) Isosceles triangles

2 sides the same
2 angles the same

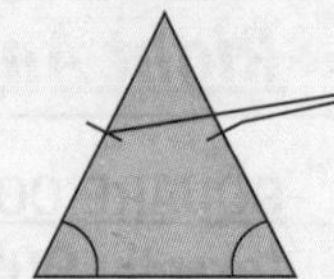

In an isosceles triangle, YOU ONLY NEED TO KNOW ONE ANGLE to be able to find the other two, which is very useful IF YOU REMEMBER IT.

a)

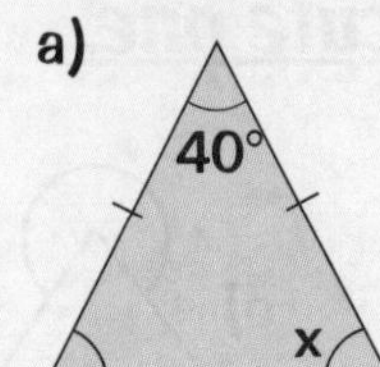

180° – 40° = 140°
The two bottom angles are both the same and they must add up to 140°, so each one must be half of 140° (= 70°). So x = 70°.

b)

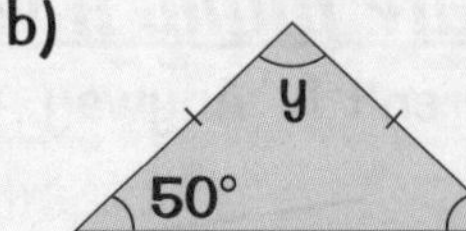

The two bottom angles must be the same, so 50° + 50° = 100°.
All the angles add up to 180° so y = 180° – 100° = 80°.

Parallel Lines

Up next — parallel lines. These make working out angles even easier. No really, they do...

Angles and Parallel Lines

Whenever one line goes across 2 parallel lines, then the two opposite angles are the same, as shown below:

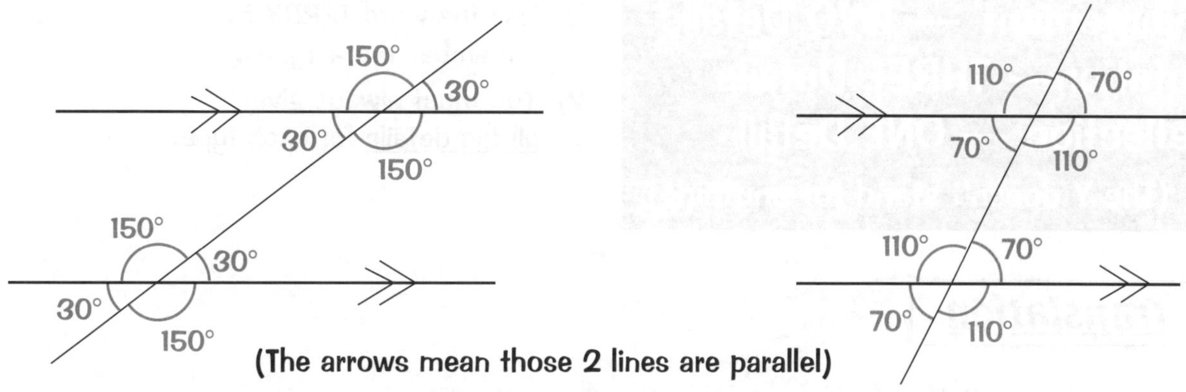

(The arrows mean those 2 lines are parallel)

Whenever you have TWO PARALLEL LINES...
1) there are only two different angles: A SMALL ONE and A BIG ONE
2) and they ALWAYS ADD UP TO 180°. E.g. 30° and 150° or 70° and 110°

The trickiest bit about parallel lines is SPOTTING THEM IN THE FIRST PLACE — watch out for these 'Z', 'C', 'U' and 'F' shapes popping up. They're a dead giveaway that you've got a pair of parallel lines.

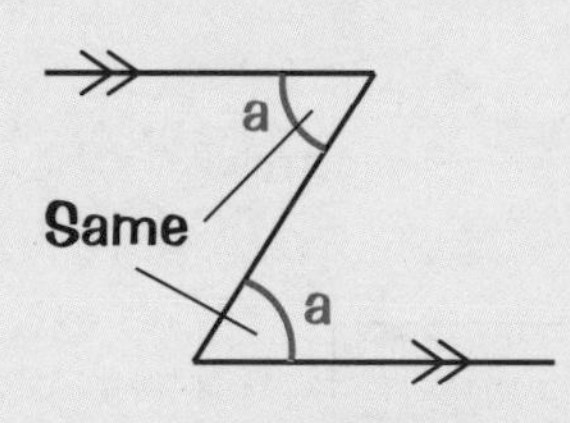

In a Z-shape they're called "ALTERNATE ANGLES"

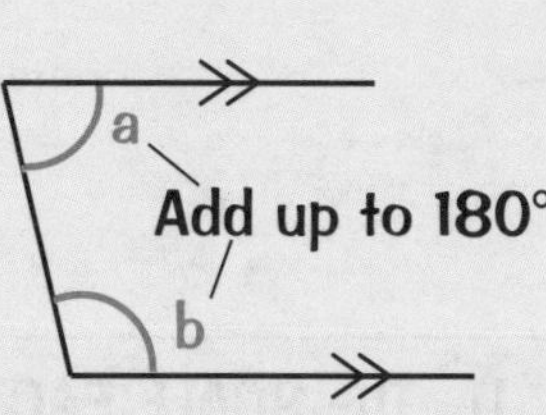

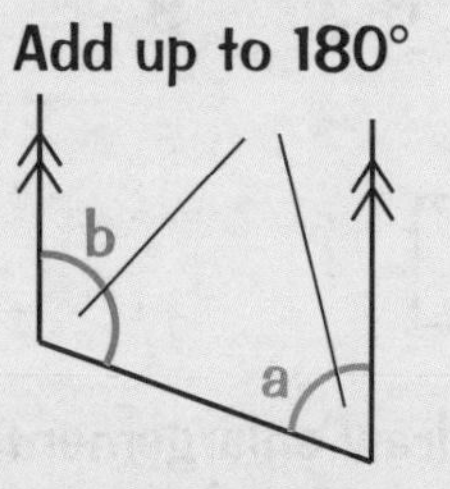

If they add up to 180° they're called "SUPPLEMENTARY ANGLES"

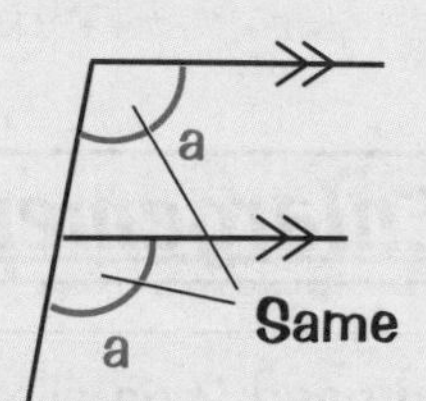

In an F-shape they're called "CORRESPONDING ANGLES"

Alas you're expected to learn these three silly names too!

I chose not to choose life. I chose parallel line spotting...

Spotting parallel lines is really, really important, so always have a good look for them. There are some questions that you won't be able to answer if you miss them. And I think we'd agree that that's a bad thing.

1) The diagram shown here has one angle given as 60°. Find all the other 7 angles.

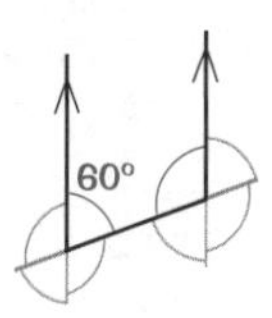

The Four Transformations

Objects can be transformed by changing their position or size, spinning or reflecting them.

Four Types of Transformation

T	ranslation — ONE Detail
E	nlargement — TWO Details
R	otation — THREE Details
R	eflection — ONE Detail
Y	(The Y doesn't stand for anything)

1) Use the word TERRY to remember the 4 types.
2) You must always give all the details for each type.

1) Translation

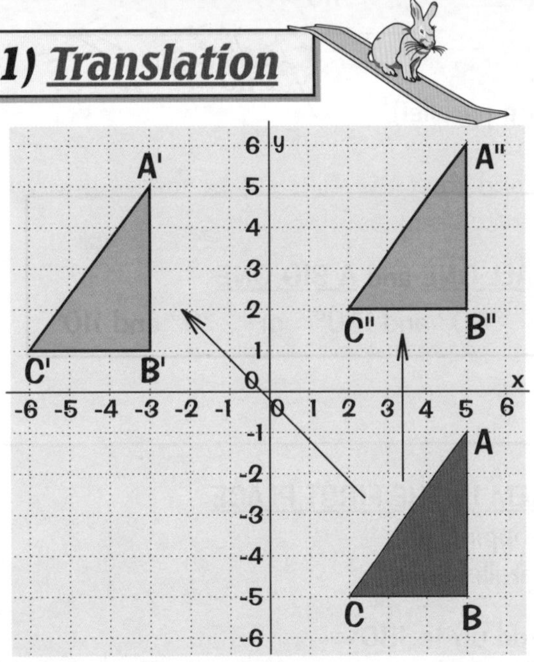

A translation is just a SLIDE. You'll be told how far along and how far up to draw the translation.

ABC to A'B'C' is a translation of 8 left and 6 up.
ABC to A''B''C'' is a translation of 7 up.

2) Enlargement

You need 2 details to draw enlargements: 1) The SCALE FACTOR
2) The CENTRE of Enlargement

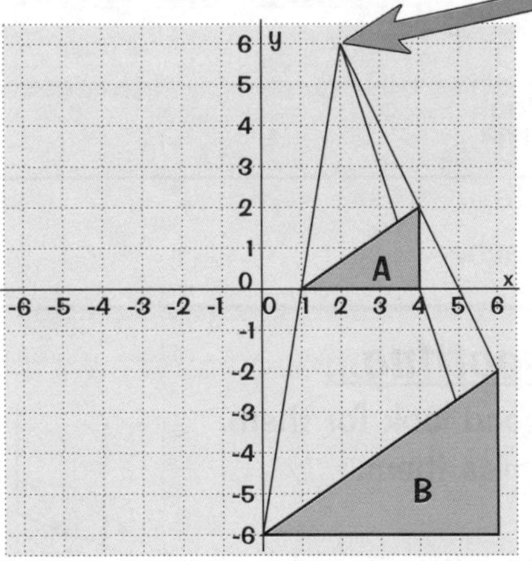

From A to B is an enlargement of scale factor 2, and centre (2,6).

N.B. Lengths are doubled, distances from the centre are doubled too.

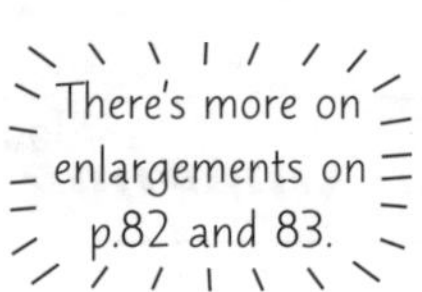

There's more on enlargements on p.82 and 83.

With enlargement, the ANGLES of the object remain unchanged. The RATIOS of the lengths of the sides, and the object's ORIENTATION remain unchanged. The size and position do change.

The Four Transformations

Two down, two to go...

3) Rotation

You need these 3 details:
1) ANGLE to turn
2) DIRECTION (Clockwise or Anti-clockwise)
3) CENTRE of Rotation

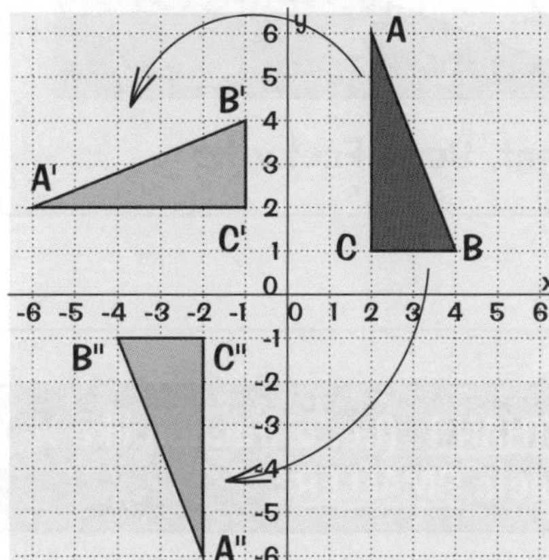

ABC to A'B'C' is a Rotation of 90°, anticlockwise, ABOUT the origin.

ABC to A"B"C" is a Rotation of half a turn (180°), clockwise, ABOUT the origin.

(For half-turns, it doesn't actually matter if you go clockwise or anticlockwise.)

The only things that change in a rotation are the POSITION and the ORIENTATION of the object. Everything else remains unchanged.

4) Reflection

You'll be given this ONE detail: The MIRROR LINE

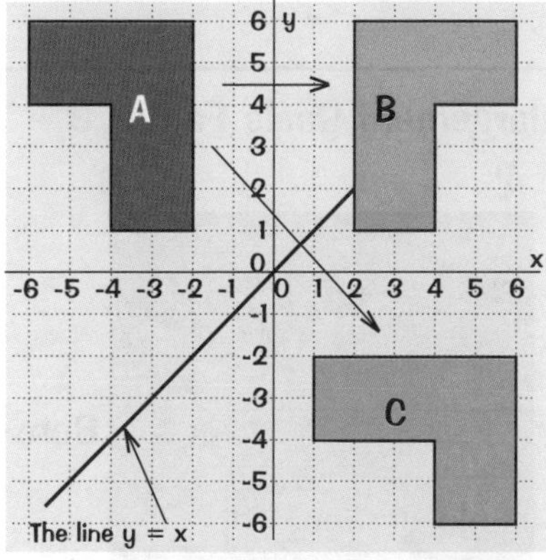

A to B is a reflection IN the y-axis.

A to C is a reflection IN the line y=x.

With reflection, the POSITION and ORIENTATION of the object are the only things that change.

Wish someone would translate these pages for me...

Another two pages down. Hurrah. Before you move on you need to:
LEARN the names of the Four Transformations and the details for each.
Then, when you think you know it, turn over and write it all down.
Finally, do a dance to celebrate. Any dance will do.

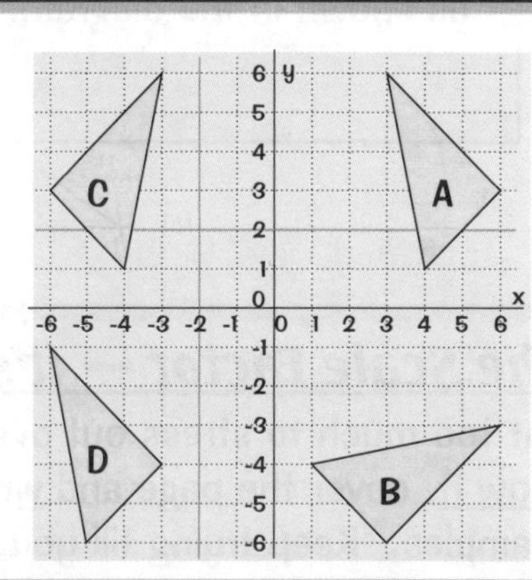

1) Describe fully these 4 transformations:

A→B, B→C, C→A, A→D

Enlargements

Enlargements are a really important type of transformation — so much so that here's an extra two pages on them, created especially for you. I know, I know, I'm too kind...

Scale Factors

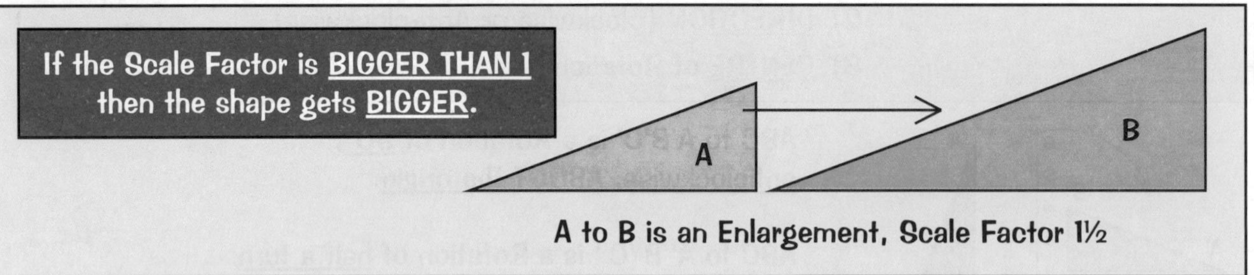

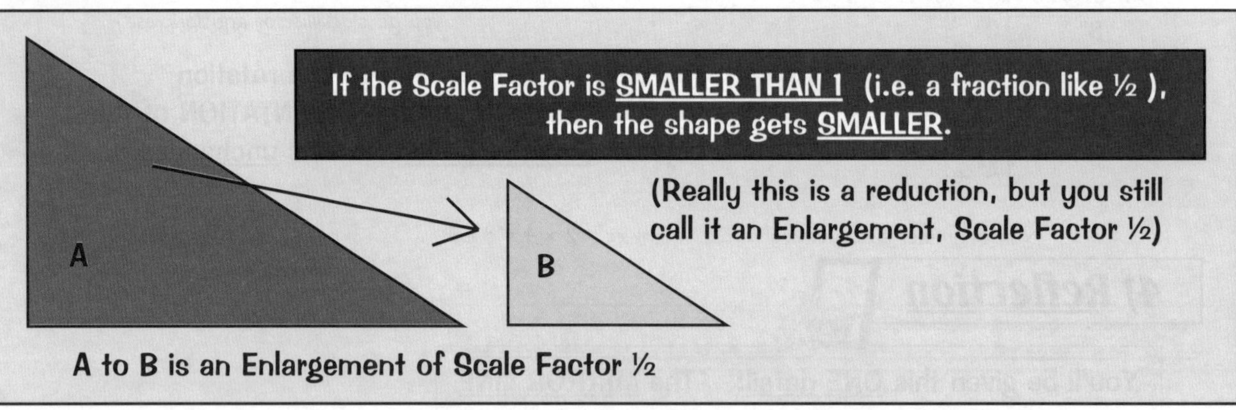

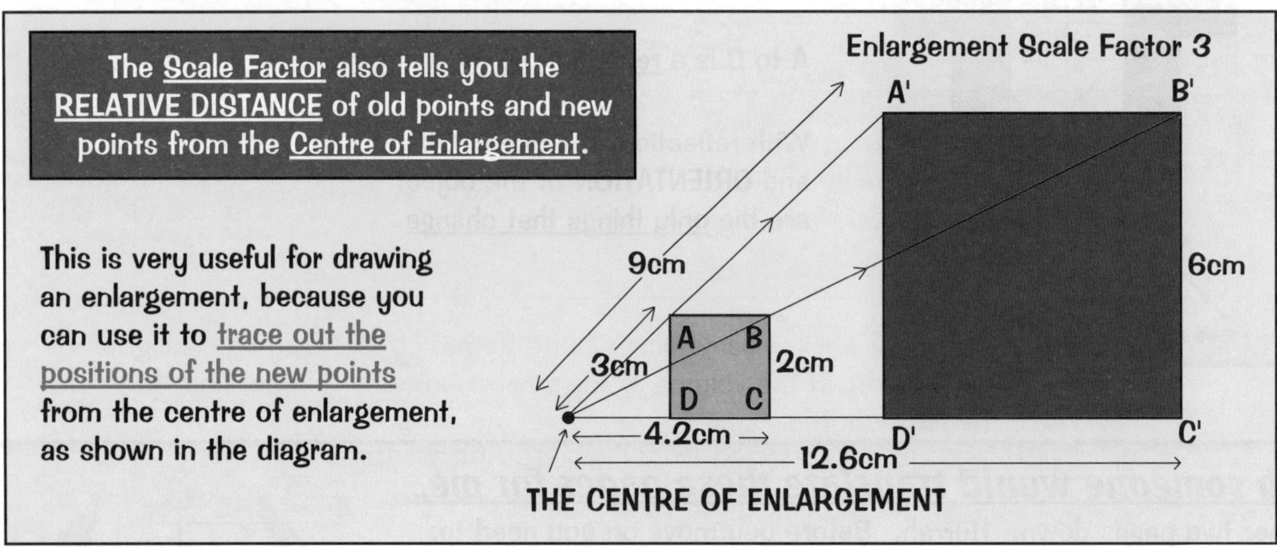

The Scale Factor — it's time... to face... the diet...

Not too much to stress out over here — LEARN everything on the page, then when you think you know it, cover the page and write it all down from memory. Make sure you include the sketches and examples. Keep trying till you can. What a fun game that'll be. I'm almost jealous. Almost...

Enlargements

More on enlargements...

Use the Formula Triangle for Calculations

The lengths of the big and small shapes are related to the Scale Factor by this very important Formula Triangle which you must learn:

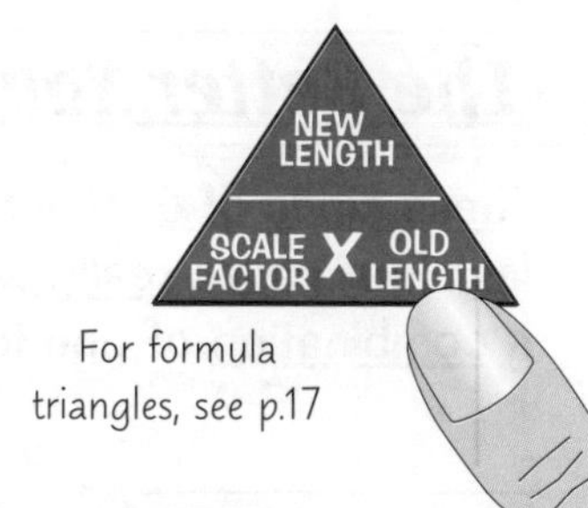

For formula triangles, see p.17

EXAMPLE: Find the missing width, x, in the diagram.

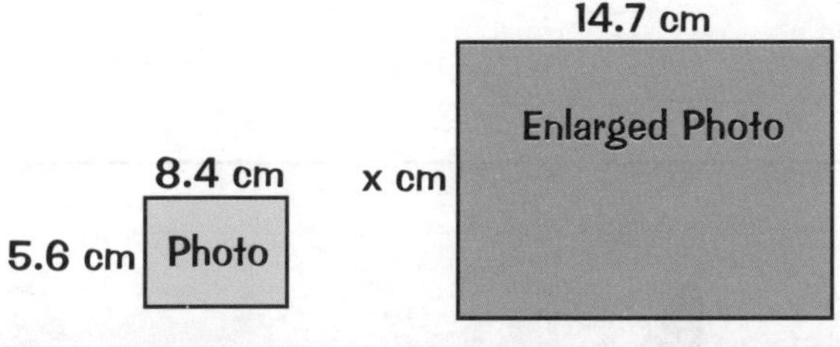

To find the width of the enlarged photo we use the formula triangle TWICE, (firstly to find the Scale Factor, and then to find the missing side):

1) Scale Factor = New length ÷ Old length = 14.7 ÷ 8.4 = 1.75
2) New width = Scale Factor × Old width = 1.75 × 5.6 = 9.8 cm

But without the formula triangle you're scuppered (Just like this fish)

Note — you can use the formula triangle to find perimeters in exactly the same way as lengths. E.g. a square with sides 1 cm is enlarged by a scale factor of 2. New perimeter = scale factor × old perimeter = 2 × 4 = 8 cm.

Areas and Volumes of Enlargements

Ho ho! This little joker catches everybody out. The increase in area and volume is BIGGER than the scale factor. For example, if the Scale Factor is 2, the lengths are twice as big, each area is 4 times as big, and the volume is 8 times as big. The rule is this:

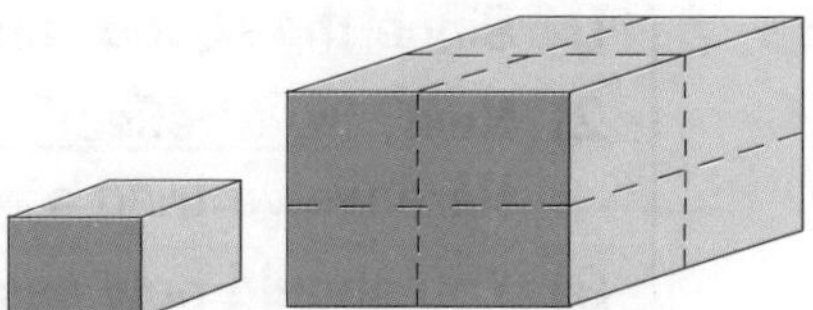

For a Scale Factor n:

The SIDES are n times bigger
The AREAS are n^2 times bigger
The VOLUMES are n^3 times bigger — Simple... but VERY FORGETTABLE

EXAMPLE: Two bottles of water are the same shape but different sizes. They have heights of 20 cm and 30 cm. If the volume of the smaller bottle is 2 litres, find the volume of the larger bottle.

1) Scale Factor n = New height ÷ Old height = 30 ÷ 20 = 1.5
2) New volume = Old volume × (Scale Factor)^3 = 2 × 1.5^3 = 6.75 litres

"Twice as much learning, 4 times better results, 8 times more fun...

...with a scale factor of 2, CGP's the guide for you". It's our new slogan. Pretty good isn't it...

1) Two triangles which are the same shape but different sizes have heights of 5 cm and 45 cm respectively. The smaller triangle has an area of 30 cm^2. Find the area of the larger triangle.
2) Two cones of the same shape but different sizes have base diameters of 20 cm and 50 cm. If the volume of the smaller one is 120 cm^3, find the volume of the other one.

Combinations of Transformations

In the Exam they might be horrid to you and stick two transformations together and ask what transformations get you from shape A to shape B. Be ready. Be prepared. Don't let them win.

The Better You Know Them All — The Easier it is

These kinds of question aren't so bad — but ONLY if you've LEARNT the four transformations on the last four pages really well — if you don't know them, then you certainly won't do too well at spotting a combination of one followed by another. That's because the method is basically 'Try it and see...'

Example:

"What combination of two transformations takes you from triangle A to triangle B?"

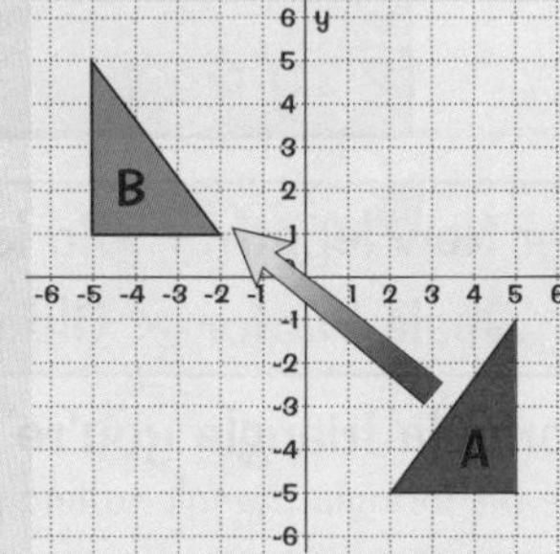

(There's usually a few different ways of getting from one shape to the other — but remember you only need to find ONE of them.)

METHOD: Try an obvious transformation first, and see...

If you think about it, the answer can only be a combination of two of the four types shown on pages 80 and 81, so you can immediately start to narrow it down:

1) Since the shapes are the same size we can rule out enlargements.
2) Next, try a reflection (in either the x-axis or the y-axis). Here we've tried a reflection in the y-axis, to give shape A':
3) You should now easily be able to see the final step from A' to B — it's a translation of 6 units up.

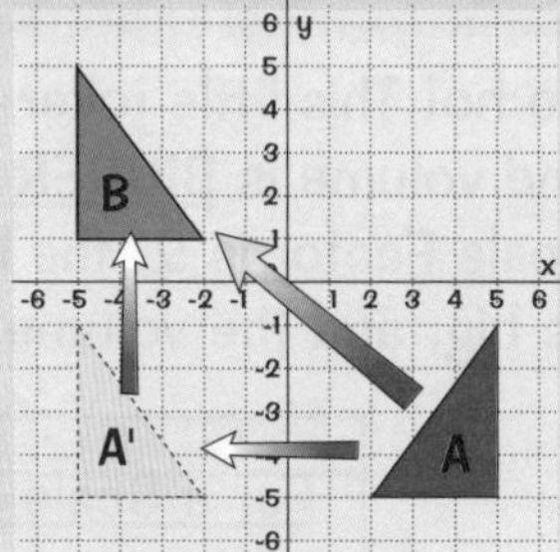

And that's it DONE — from A to B is simply a combination of:

A reflection in the y-axis followed by a translation of 6 units up.

At least that's one answer anyway. If instead we decided to reflect it in the x-axis first (as shown here) then we'd get another answer (see questions below) — but both are right.

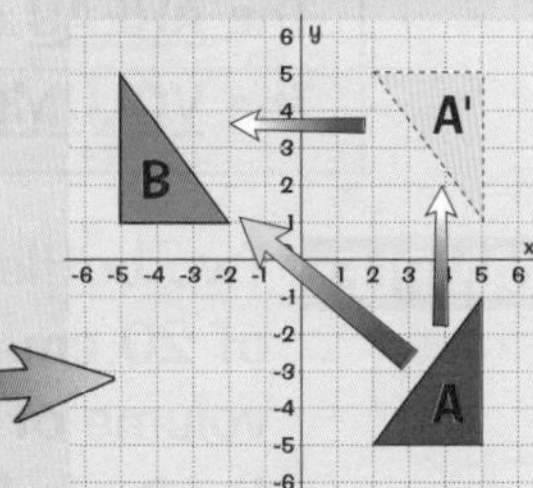

Not bothered about shapes — how do I get from one topic to another...

Seriously, enough with all the transformations. We'll make this the last page.

1) What pair of transformations will convert shape C into shape D?: What pair will convert shape D to shape C?
2) In the example above, find the other transformation needed to get to shape B after reflecting shape A in the x-axis.

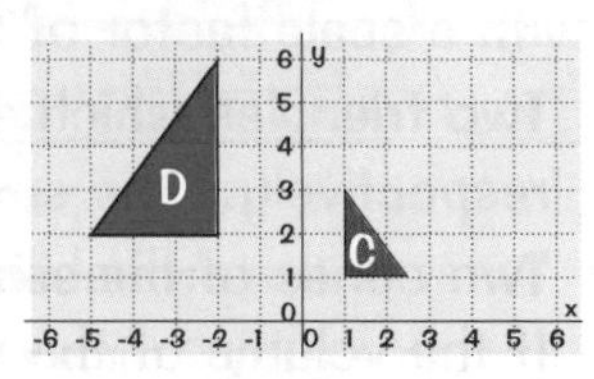

Probability

Probability definitely seems a bit of a 'Black Art' to most people. It's not as bad as you think, but YOU MUST LEARN THE BASIC FACTS, which is what we have on these 4 pages.

All Probabilities are between 0 and 1

Probabilities can only have values from 0 to 1 (including those values). You should be able to put the probability of any event happening on this scale of 0 to 1.

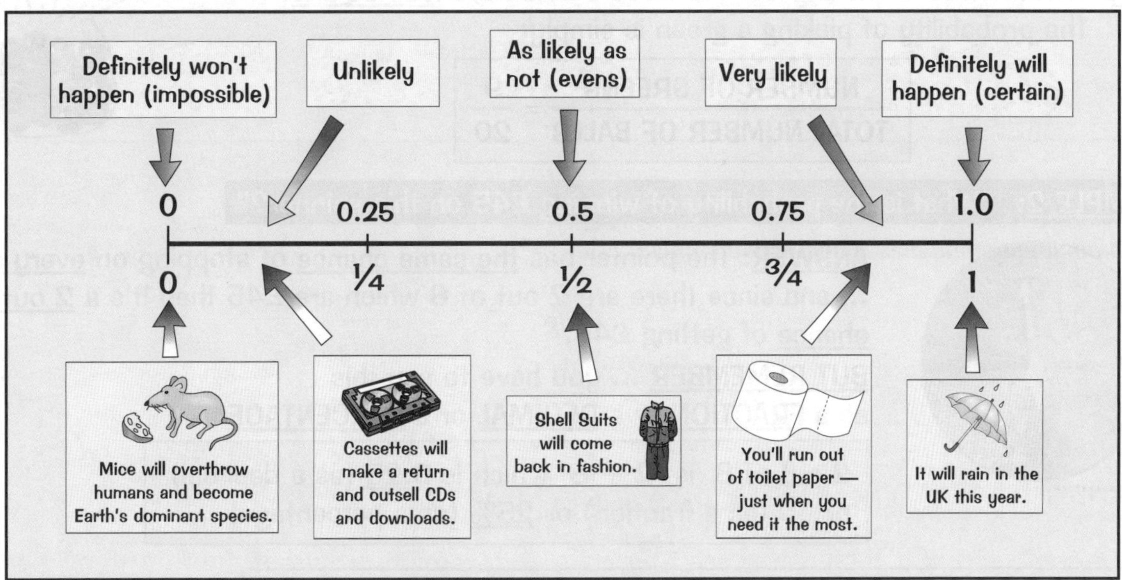

Remember you can give probabilities using FRACTIONS, DECIMALS or PERCENTAGES.

Equal Probabilities

When the different results all have the same chance of happening, then the probabilities will be EQUAL. These are the two cases which usually come up in Exams:

I hope they don't ask me to toss this.

1) TOSSING A COIN: Equal chance of getting a head or a tail (probability = $\frac{1}{2}$)

2) THROWING A DICE: Equal chance of getting any of the numbers (probability = $\frac{1}{6}$)

The probability of death and taxes is 1...

Picking cards from a pack is another example of equal probabilities, and it might come up in your exam.

1) What is the probability of picking an ace of any suit from a shuffled deck of cards (no jokers)? (remember, it's 52 cards in a pack).

Probability

There's more to probability than just tossing coins and rolling dice you know. Oh yes.

Unequal Probabilities

These make for more interesting questions. (Which means you'll get them in the Exam.)

EXAMPLE 1: "A bag contains 6 blue balls, 5 red balls and 9 green balls. Find the probability of picking out a green ball."

ANSWER: The chances of picking out the three colours are NOT EQUAL.
The probability of picking a green is simply:

$$\frac{\text{NUMBER OF GREENS}}{\text{TOTAL NUMBER OF BALLS}} = \frac{9}{20}$$

EXAMPLE 2: "What is the probability of winning £45 on this spinner?"

ANSWER: The pointer has the same chance of stopping on every sector... ... and since there are 2 out of 8 which are £45 then it's a 2 out of 8 chance of getting £45.

BUT REMEMBER ... you have to say this as a FRACTION or a DECIMAL or a PERCENTAGE:

2 out of 8 is 2 ÷ 8 which is 0.25 (as a decimal) or $\frac{1}{4}$ (as a fraction) or 25% (as a percentage)

The Probability of the Opposite happening is just the rest of the probability that's left over

This is simple enough AS LONG AS YOU REMEMBER IT.
If the probability of something happening is, say, 0.3 then the chance of it NOT HAPPENING is 1 – 0.3 (= 0.7), i.e. it's what's left when you subtract it from 1.

Example: A loaded dice has a 0.25 chance of coming up TWO. What is the chance of it not coming up TWO?

Answer: 1 – 0.25 = 0.75. So, the chance of the dice not coming up TWO is 0.75.

Listing All Outcomes: 2 Coins, Dice, Spinners

A simple question you might get is to list all the possible results from tossing two coins or two spinners or a dice and a spinner, etc. Whatever it is, it'll be very similar to these, so LEARN THEM:

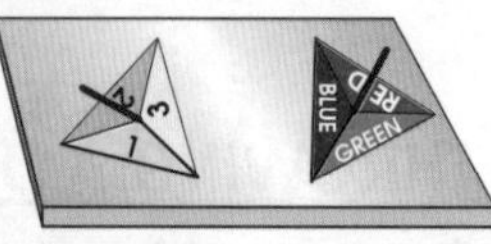

The possible outcomes from TOSSING TWO COINS are:

HH HT TH TT

From TWO SPINNERS with 3 sides:

BLUE, 1	RED, 1	GREEN, 1
BLUE, 2	RED, 2	GREEN, 2
BLUE, 3	RED, 3	GREEN, 3

Try and list the possible outcomes METHODICALLY — to make sure you get them ALL.

Spinners fashion tip #56 — gold hot pants are an absolute must......

Spinners and bags of balls come up a lot in the exam. Don't panic if they use another example — you work it out in exactly the same way. Try this one: 1) What is the probability of picking a white puppy from a bag containing 3 black puppies, 4 brown puppies, 2 white puppies and one purple puppy?

Probability

This is where most people start getting into trouble, and d'you know why?
I'll tell you — it's because they don't know the three simple steps and the two rules to apply:

Three Simple Steps

1) Always break down a complicated-looking probability question into A SEQUENCE of SEPARATE SINGLE EVENTS.
2) Find the probability of EACH of these SEPARATE SINGLE EVENTS.
3) Apply the AND/OR rule:

And now for the rules...

1) The AND Rule:

$$P(A \text{ and } B) = P(A) \times P(B)$$

Which means:

The probability of Event A AND Event B BOTH happening is equal to the two separate probabilities MULTIPLIED together.

(strictly speaking, the two events have to be INDEPENDENT. All that means is that one event happening does not in any way affect the other one happening. Contrast this with mutually exclusive below.)

2) The OR Rule:

$$P(A \text{ or } B) = P(A) + P(B)$$

Which means:

The probability of EITHER Event A OR Event B happening is equal to the two separate probabilities ADDED together.

(Strictly speaking, the two events have to be MUTUALLY EXCLUSIVE which means that if one event happens, the other one can't happen.)

The way to remember this is that it's the wrong way round — i.e. you'd want the AND to go with the + but it doesn't: It's 'AND with ×' and 'OR with +'.

Example

"Find the probability of picking two kings from a pack of cards (assuming you don't replace the first card picked)."

1) SPLIT this into TWO SEPARATE EVENTS — i.e. picking the first king and then picking the second king.
2) Find the SEPARATE probabilities of these two separate events:
   P(1st king) $= \frac{4}{52}$ P(2nd king) $= \frac{3}{51}$ (— note the change from 52 to 51)
3) Apply the AND/OR rule: BOTH events must happen, so it's the AND rule:
   so multiply the two separate probabilities: $\frac{4}{52} \times \frac{3}{51} = \frac{1}{221}$

The fish survived. Hurrah.

Revise — and/or eat cake...

Wowsers, lots of important stuff on those two pages. Learn the three simple steps for multiple events, and the AND/OR rule and you'll be fine and/or dandy in the exam. Ahem. Now try these jokers...

1) Find the probability of picking from a pack of cards (without replacement):
   a) A queen followed by a jack. b) Two hearts in a row.

Probability — Relative Frequency

This isn't the number of times your granny comes to visit. It's a way of estimating probabilities. Since you asked, my granny visits twice a year. She says she'd like to visit more, but sleeping on the blow-up bed plays mischief with her bad back.

Fair or Biased?

The probability of rolling a five on a dice is $\frac{1}{6}$ — you know that each of the 6 numbers on a dice is equally likely to be rolled, and there's only 1 five.

BUT this only works if it's a fair dice. If the dice is a bit wonky (the technical term is 'biased') then each number won't have an equal chance of being rolled. That's where Relative Frequency comes in — you can use it to estimate probabilities when things might be wonky.

Do the Experiment Again and Again and Again and Again

You need to do an experiment over and over again and then do a quick calculation. (Remember, an experiment could just mean rolling a dice.)
Usually the results of these experiments will be written in a table.

The Formula for Relative Frequency

$$\text{Probability of something happening} = \frac{\text{Number of times it has happened}}{\text{Number of times you tried}}$$

You can work out the relative frequency as a fraction but usually decimals are best.

The important thing to remember is:

The more times you do the experiment, the more accurate the probability will be.

Example:

Number of Times the dice was rolled	10	20	50	100
Number of threes rolled	2	5	11	23
Relative Frequency	$\frac{2}{10} = 0.2$	$\frac{5}{20} = 0.25$	$\frac{11}{50} = 0.22$	$\frac{23}{100} = 0.23$

So, what's the probability? We've got 4 possible answers, but the best estimate is the one worked out using the highest number of dice rolls. This makes the probability of rolling a three on this dice 0.23.

And since for a fair, unbiased dice, the probability of rolling a three is $\frac{1}{6}$ (about 0.17), then our dice is probably biased.

Dice rolls — a crunchy pack lunch alternative...

Blast those wonky dice. That's what started all this. Still it's all bound to come up on the exam. So...

1) A 3-sided spinner is spun 100 times – it lands on red 43 times, blue 24 times and green the other times. Calculate the relative frequency of each outcome.

Revision Summary for Unit Two — 2

WHAT YOU'RE SUPPOSED TO DO HERE is put all the methods you've learned in the second half of Unit Two into practice, and answer these lovely questions.

1) What are the three types of symmetry?

2) Sharon is making some sample birthday cards for a stationery company. She wants to fold each card along a line of symmetry, so it folds exactly together. Draw all the lines of symmetry for each of the card designs.
a)  b) 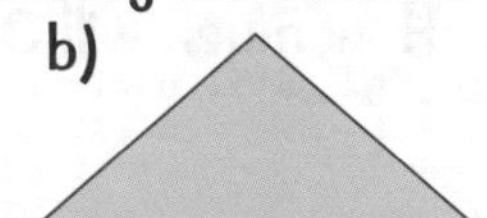 c) 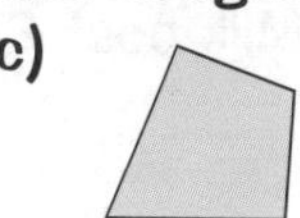 d) 

3) If a circle has a diameter of 12 m, what is its radius?

4) Draw a circle and then show on it a tangent, a chord and an arc.

5) An architect is planning an extension to a house, shown on the right.
Using the scale 1 m : 1 cm, draw:
a) the side elevation b) the front elevation c) the plan view.

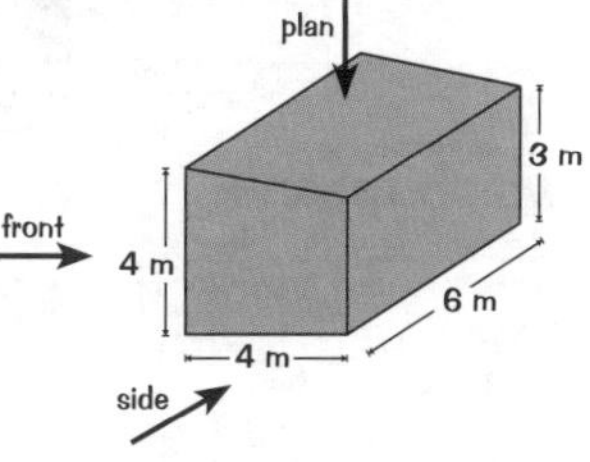

6) Do a sketch of these four solids and draw the net for each one:
a) A cube b) A cuboid c) A triangular prism d) A square-based pyramid

7) Draw these four special angles:
a) 90° b) 180° c) 270° d) 360°

8) Work out angles X and Y in the diagram:

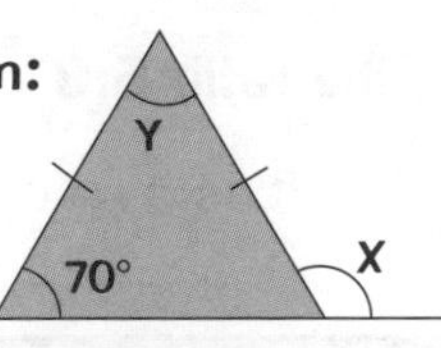

9) What transformation maps:
a) shape A onto shape B? b) shape C onto shape D?

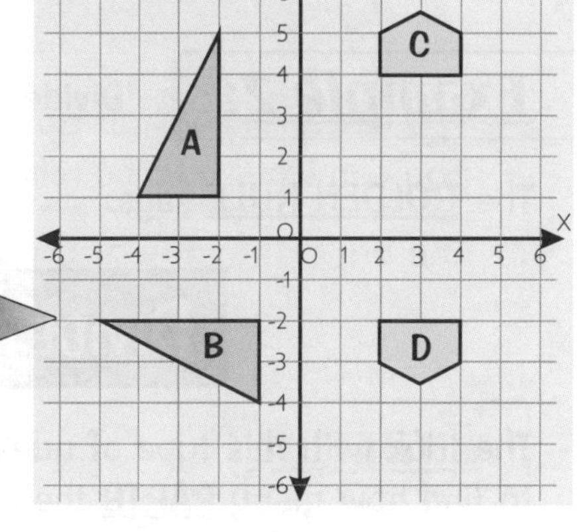

10) Julie wants a picture enlarging for a new frame.
Use the diagram to work out the enlargement scale factor Julie needs.

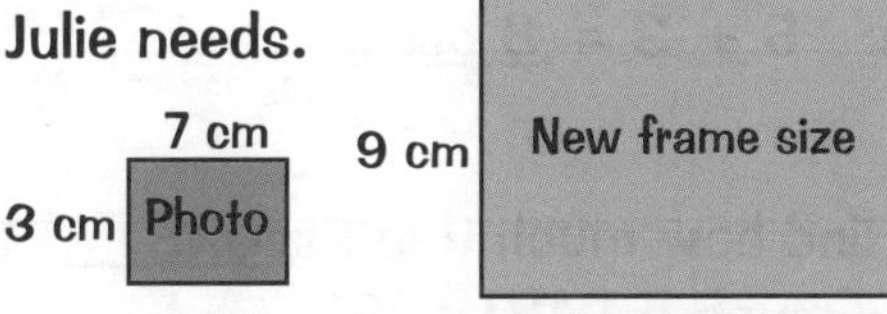

11) Colin is designing a game for the school summer fair. He wants the players to have a 50% chance of winning. He has a bag containing 3 red balls, 5 green balls and 7 black balls.
If you pick out a red or green ball you win a prize.
a) What is the % chance of winning Colin's game?
b) How can he change the game so that there's a 50% chance of winning?

12) If I toss 2 coins, list all the possible outcomes. Since all these outcomes are equally likely, what is the chance of getting two heads?

13) If I toss a coin and throw a dice, list all the possible outcomes and say what the probability is of me getting a HEAD and a SIX.

14) The probability of a biased dice giving a SIX is 0.2.
What is the chance of it NOT giving a six?

Ratio in the Home

Unit Three kicks off with ratios. And there's some good news here — lots of Exam questions which at first sight seem completely different can actually all be done using the GOLDEN RULE...

DIVIDE FOR ONE, THEN TIMES FOR ALL

Example 1:

"5 pints of Milk cost £1.30. How much will 3 pints cost?"

The GOLDEN RULE says:

DIVIDE FOR ONE, THEN TIMES FOR ALL

which means:

Divide the price by 5 to find how much FOR ONE PINT, then multiply by 3 to find how much FOR 3 PINTS.

So...

£1.30 ÷ 5 = 0.26 = 26p (for 1 pint)
×3 = 78p (for 3 pints)

Example 2:

"Divide £400 in the ratio 5:3"

The GOLDEN RULE says:

DIVIDE FOR ONE, THEN TIMES FOR ALL

The trick with this type of question is to add together the numbers in the RATIO to find how many PARTS there are: 5 + 3 = 8 parts.

Now use The Golden Rule:

Divide the £400 by 8 to find how much it is for ONE PART, then multiply by 5 and by 3 to find how much 5 PARTS ARE and how much 3 PARTS ARE.

So...

£400 ÷ 8 = £50 (for 1 part)
×5 = £250 (for 5 parts)
×3 = £150 (for 3 parts)

So £400 split in the ratio 5:3 is £250 : £150

The Three Mathsketeers say "divide for one, then times for all"...

Smug gits. It's a simple rule — the trick is knowing when to use it. Learning the examples above will help.

1) If seven pencils cost 98p, how much will 4 pencils cost?
2) Divide £2400 in the ratio 5:7.

Ratio — Rat 'n' Toad Pie

Example 3 — The Recipe

"The following recipe is for 'Froggatt's Homespun Rat 'n' Toad Pie' and serves 4 people.

4 Freshly-caught Rats (frozen will do)
2 Common Toads (minus warts)
5 Ounces of 'Froggatt's Lumpy Sprout Ketchup'
8 Soiled Potatoes
A big wodge of pastry

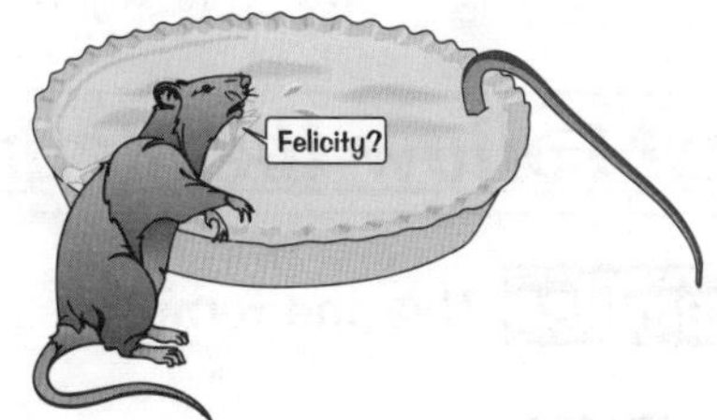

Change these amounts so there's enough for SIX people."

Answer

The GOLDEN RULE says:

DIVIDE FOR ONE, THEN TIMES FOR ALL

which means:

DIVIDE each amount to get enough for one person,
then TIMES to get enough for SIX.

Since the recipe is for 4 people then DIVIDE EACH AMOUNT BY 4 to find the amount for 1 person — then MULTIPLY THAT BY 6 to find how much for 6 people — simple enough:

4 Rats ÷ 4 = 1 Rat (for one person) ×6 = 6 Rats (for 6 people)

2 Toads ÷ 4 = 0.5 Toad (for one person) ×6 = 3 Toads (for 6 people)

5 Ounces of 'Froggatt's Lumpy Sprout Ketchup' ÷ 4
= 1.25 Ounces (for one person) ×6 = 7.5 Ounces (for 6 people)

8 'taties ÷ 4 = 2 'taties (for one person) ×6 = 12 'taties (for 6 people)

A big wodge of pastry ÷ 4 then ×6 = A wodge of pastry half as big again.

In fact, all the amounts are just HALF AS MUCH AGAIN, if you notice.

If there was badger and mole in this pie too it might give you wind...

...in the willows fever. A terrible illness where sufferers believe they are a British woodland animal... and have an overwhelming desire to wear tweed. Right, it's time to test whether you've really learnt the Golden Rule: Work out the amount of each ingredient needed to make enough Rat 'n' Toad pie for 9 people.*

*If you could e-mail me your answer, that would be great — I'm holding a dinner party next Saturday.

More Substituting into Formulas

In GCSE Maths, you're often asked to use formulas like this one:

$$F = \frac{9}{5}C + 32$$

It looks scary — but this topic is a lot easier than you think...

Just Follow the Method

Example: Use the formula above to convert 15 °C from Celsius (C) into Fahrenheit (F).

Method:

1) Write out the Formula — e.g. $F = \frac{9}{5}C + 32$
2) Write it again, directly underneath, but substituting numbers for letters on the RHS. (Right Hand Side) — $F = \frac{9}{5}15 + 32$
3) Work it out IN STAGES. Use BODMAS (see p.2) to work things out IN THE RIGHT ORDER. WRITE DOWN values for each bit as you go along. — $F = 27 + 32$, $= 59$, $F = 59°$
4) DO NOT attempt to do it all in one go on your calculator. That ridiculous method fails at least 50% of the time.

If you don't follow this STRICT METHOD you'll just keep getting them wrong — it's as simple as that.

Example: A mysterious quantity T, is given by: $T = (P - 7)^2 + 4R/Q$
Find the value of T when P = 4, Q = -2 and R = 3

1) Write down the formula: $T = (P - 7)^2 + 4R/Q$
2) Put the numbers in: $T = (4 - 7)^2 + 4\times3/-2$
3) Then work it out in stages:
$= (-3)^2 + 4\times3/-2$
$= 9 + 4\times3/-2$
$= 9 + 12/-2$
$= 9 + -6$
$= 9 - 6 = \underline{3}$

Note BODMAS in operation: Brackets worked out first, then squared. Multiplications and divisions done before finally adding and subtracting.

Really tricky calculations can be a right pain in the BODMAS...

LEARN the 4 Steps of the Substitution Method and then turn over and write it all down from memory. Go on. Go ooooooon. Go on go on go on.

1) Practise the above examples until you can do them easily without help.
2) If $C = \frac{5}{9}(F - 32)$, find the value of C when F = 77.

Trial and Improvement

Back in Unit 2 you learned how to solve linear equations. In Unit 3, you need to be able to solve quadratic and cubic equations as well as the linear ones. Here's a good method for finding approximate answers to equations that don't have simple whole number answers. It boils down to trial and error, but there's a clear method which you must learn if you want to get it right...

See pages 67 and 68 for solving linear equations.

Method

1) SUBSTITUTE TWO INITIAL VALUES into the equation that give OPPOSITE CASES.
2) Choose your next value IN BETWEEN the previous two, and PUT IT into the equation.
3) After only 3 or 4 steps you should have 2 NUMBERS which are to the right degree of accuracy but DIFFER BY 1 IN THE LAST DIGIT.
4) Now take the EXACT MIDDLE VALUE to decide which is the answer you want.

Opposite cases means one answer too big, one too small. If they don't give opposite cases try again.

Continue the process, choosing new values between the two closest opposite cases, (and preferably nearer to the one which is closer to the answer you want).

E.g. if you had to get your answer to 2 DP, you'd eventually end up with say 5.43 and 5.44, with these giving OPPOSITE cases.

E.g. for 5.43 and 5.44, you'd try 5.435 to see if the real answer was between 5.43 and 5.435 or between 5.435 and 5.44.

Example

"The equation $x^3 + x = 40$ has a solution between 3 and 3.5. Find this solution to 1 DP"

Try $x = 3$ $\quad 3^3 + 3 = 30$ (Too small)
Try $x = 3.5$ $\quad 3.5^3 + 3.5 = 46.375$ (Too big)

← (2 opposite cases)

40 is what we want and it's closer to 46.375 than it is to 30 so we'll choose our next value for x closer to 3.5 than 3.

Try $x = 3.3$ $\quad 3.3^3 + 3.3 = 39.237$ (Too small)

Good, this is very close, but we need to see if 3.4 is still too big or too small:

Try $x = 3.4$ $\quad 3.4^3 + 3.4 = 42.704$ (Too big)

Good, now we know that the answer must be between 3.3 and 3.4.
To find out which one it's nearest to, we have to try the EXACT MIDDLE VALUE: 3.35

Try $x = 3.35$ $\quad 3.35^3 + 3.35 = 40.945$ (Too big)

This tells us with certainty that the solution must be between 3.3 (too small) and 3.35 (too big), and so to 1 DP it must round down to 3.3. ANSWER = 3.3

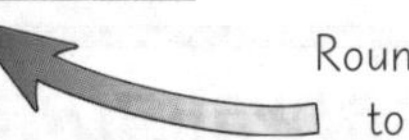

Rounding is covered in Unit 1, but you need to know it for Unit 3 too — see p6-7.

If at first you don't succeed — improve and trial again...

To get this method nailed, you must learn the 4 steps above. Do it now, and practise until you can write them down without having to look back at them. I said now. I can still see you — do it now!
The equation $x^3 - 2x = 1$ has a solution between 1 and 2. Find it to 1 DP.

Travel Graphs, Speed and Density

Woah, what's this I see — travel graphs, speed and density all on the one page? Madness...

Travel Graphs

1) A TRAVEL GRAPH is always DISTANCE (↑) against TIME (→)
2) FLAT SECTIONS are where it's STOPPED.
3) The STEEPER the graph the FASTER it's going.
4) The graph GOING UP means it's travelling AWAY. The graph COMING DOWN means it's COMING BACK AGAIN.

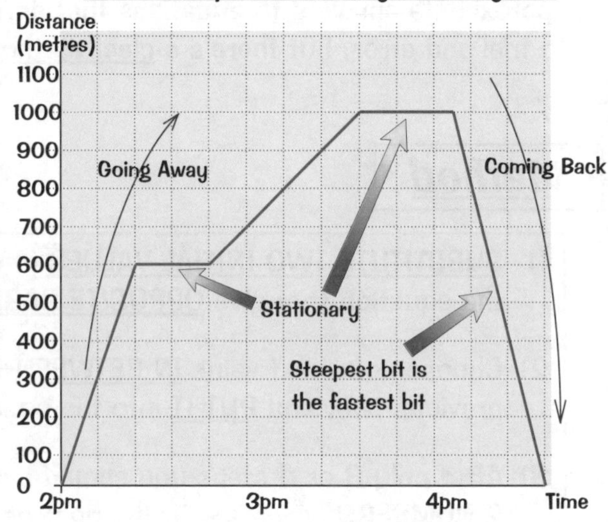

Speed = Distance ÷ Time

You can use travel graphs to calculate speeds for different sections of a journey — just read the distance and the time off the graph, then plug the numbers into the formula. There's even a formula triangle to help you remember it.

See pages 17 and 18 for more on speed.

Density = Mass ÷ Volume

The standard formula for density is:

Density = Mass ÷ Volume

so we can put it in a FORMULA TRIANGLE like this:

One way or another you must remember this formula for density, because they won't give it to you. The best method by far is to remember the order of the letters in the formula triangle as $D^{M}V$ or DiMoV (The Russian Agent).

Find the volume of an object which has a mass of 40 g and a density of 6.4 g/cm³

ANSWER: To find volume, cover up V in the formula triangle.
This leaves M/D showing, so V = M ÷ D
= 40÷6.4
= 6.25 cm³

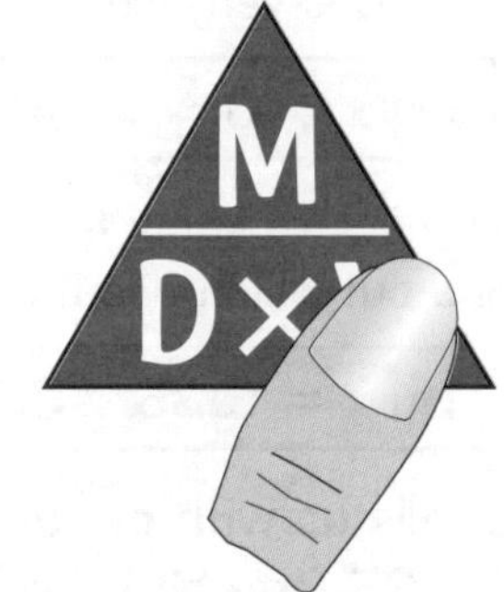

Formula for success — always butter your bread on the right side...

Make sure you've got your head around travel graphs and you've learned the two formula triangles. Then have a go at these:

1) What's the formula for Density?
2) A metal object has a volume of 45 cm³ and a mass of 743 g. What is its density?
3) Another piece of the same metal has a volume of 36.5 cm³. What is its mass?

Revision Summary for Unit Three — 1

YOU KNOW WHAT TO DO HERE — use all the super-clever mathematical knowledge you've learned in the first part of Unit 3 to answer these questions. Enjoy.

1) What is The Golden Rule for Ratio in the Home?

2) Last week Rick ordered 5 pints of milk from the milkman. His bill was £2.35. This week he orders 3 pints of milk. How much will this week's bill be?

3) Sarah is ordering new stock for her clothes shop. The shop usually sells red and blue scarves in the ratio 5:8. Sarah orders 150 red scarves. How many blue scarves should she order?

4) Ellen's thermometer only measures in Celsius (°C) but her dad can only understand temperatures in Fahrenheit (°F). She knows that to get a temperature in °F you need to 'times the temperature in °C by 9/5 and then add 32'.
   a) Write out a formula for changing °C into °F.
   b) Use your formula to find the temperature for Ellen's dad when it is 30 °C.

5) If $x^2 = 30$, find x accurate to one decimal place. (Trial and Improvement)

6) The travel graph shown on the right relates to a wandering goat ambling along a road. Describe what the goat is doing
   a) Between 4 pm and 6 pm
   b) Between 6 pm and 7 pm
   c) How far from home does the goat stray?

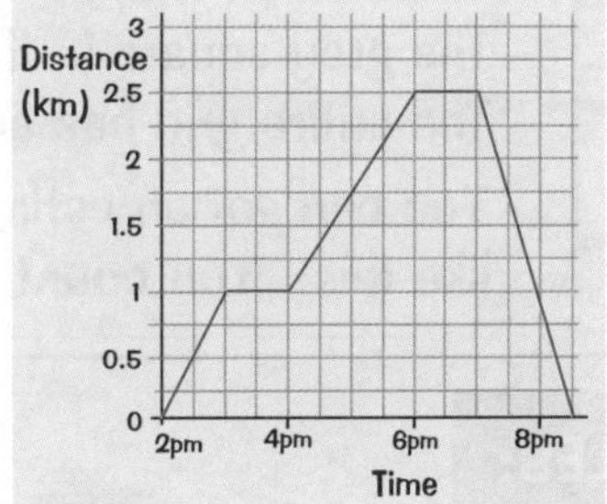

7) Fat Nigel the cat has a mass of 20 kg and an average density of 0.7 g / cm³. Calculate his volume in cm³ to 2 significant figures.

Polygons and Estimating Areas

I can almost hear you thinking "Polygons, hmmm, they sound familiar". And they are — you came across them in Unit 2. Areas have cropped up before as well. Here's some new stuff on both of 'em.

Polygons Have Interior and Exterior Angles

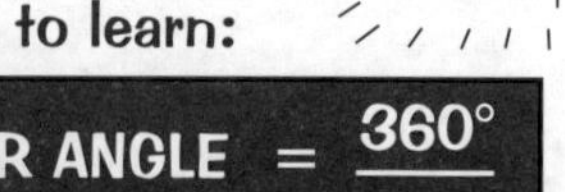

1) Exterior Angles

2) Interior Angles

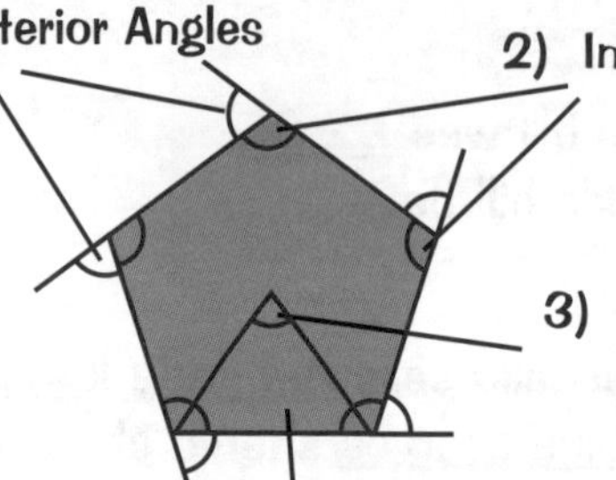

3) This angle is always the same as the Exterior Angles.

4) Each sector triangle is <u>ISOSCELES</u>.

There are 4 formulas to learn:

$$\text{EXTERIOR ANGLE} = \frac{360^\circ}{n}$$

$$\text{INTERIOR ANGLE} = 180^\circ - \text{EXTERIOR ANGLE}$$

$$\text{SUM OF EXTERIOR ANGLES} = 360^\circ$$

$$\text{SUM OF INTERIOR ANGLES} = (n - 2) \times 180^\circ$$

Note — the two SUM formulas work for <u>any</u> polygons, the top two formulas only work for <u>regular</u> polygons (see p.74).

(n is the number of sides)

Estimating Areas of Irregular Shapes

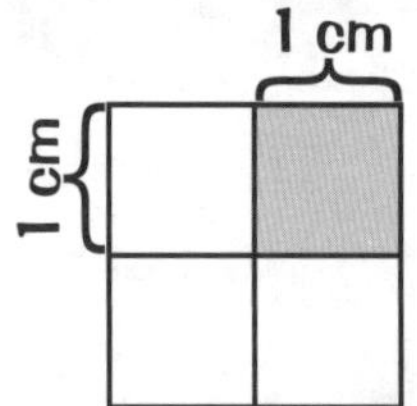

The <u>area</u> of a <u>flat shape</u> is the amount of <u>space inside</u> it.
The area of shapes is usually measured in <u>cm^2</u> or <u>m^2</u>.
The grey square in this grid measures 1 cm by 1 cm, so its area is $1 \times 1 = 1 cm^2$.
The entire grid has an area of $2 \times 2 = 4 cm^2$.

You can get an estimate of odd shapes by <u>counting squares</u> on a grid like this. You count the squares that are <u>more than half</u> covered.

EXAMPLES:

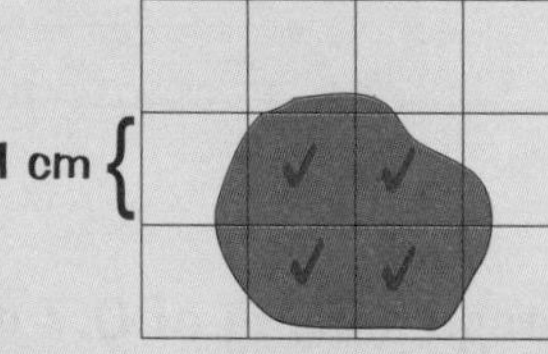

Only the <u>four</u> squares with <u>ticks</u> in are more than half covered by this boring blue blob, so the area is near enough 4 cm².

This footprint left by a lesser spotted Cumbrian Yeti has <u>two</u> squares that it <u>more than half</u> covers.
So its area is about 2 cm².

1 cm

As if estimating areas wasn't enough, you need to know the stuff on calculating areas that you learned for Unit 1 — see p28-29. Oh yeah, and you also need to know about perimeters (p27) and volumes (p30) again too. Sorry about that.

EXCLUSIVE: Heptagon lottery winner says "I'm still just a regular guy"...

This page isn't too bad — just make sure you learn the angle formulas really really well.

1) Work out the two key angles for a regular pentagon
2) And for a 12-sided regular polygon.
3) Estimate the area of the shape on the right.

1 cm

Congruence and Similarity

Shapes can be similar or congruent. And I bet you really want to know what that means — I can already picture your eager face. Well, lucky you — I've written a page all about it.

Congruent — Same Shape, Same Size

Congruence is another ridiculous maths word which sounds really complicated but it's not:

If two shapes are CONGRUENT, they are simply THE SAME — the SAME SIZE and the SAME SHAPE.

That's all it is. Just make sure you know the word.

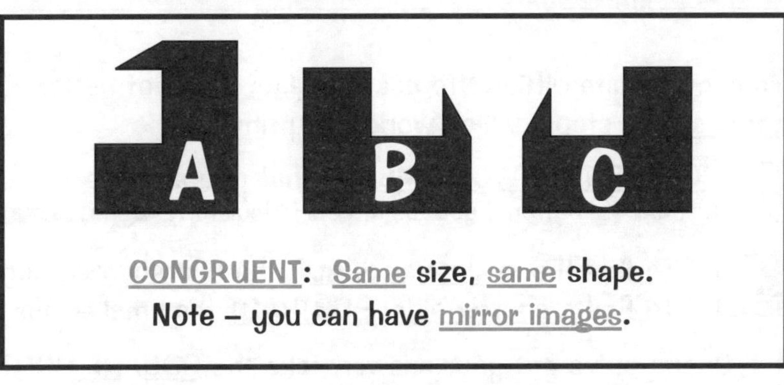

Similar — Same Shape, Different Size

Similar has a special meaning in maths, but nothing complicated:

If two shapes are SIMILAR they are exactly the SAME SHAPE but DIFFERENT SIZES.

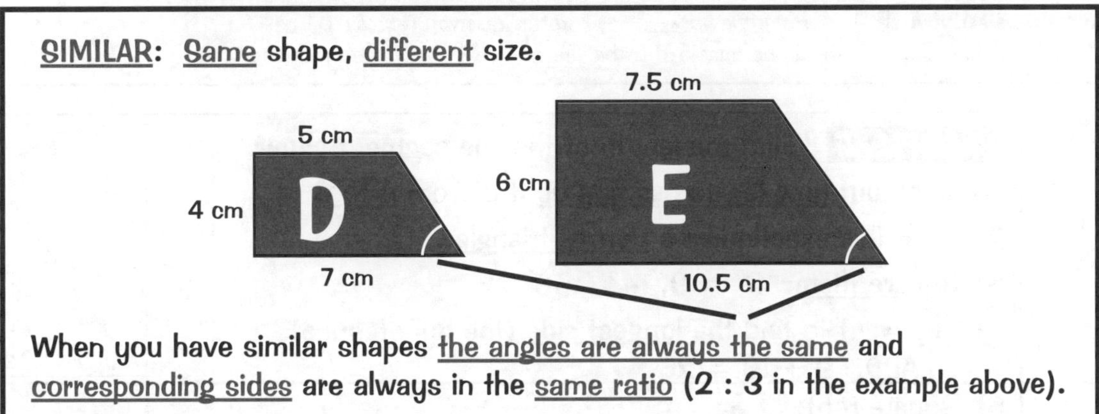

Two similar shapes can be seen as an 'enlargement'... see p82-83.

Pizza and a frisbee — same shape and size but don't get them confused...

Know what congruence and similar mean inside-out — it's important you don't get them mixed up.

1) a) Which of these four shapes are similar?
   b) Which are congruent?

i)  ii) 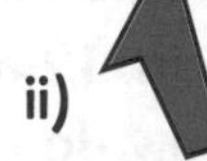 iii) 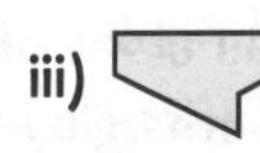 iv) 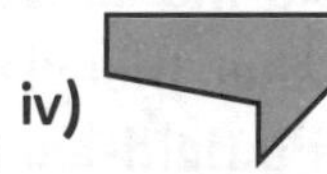

Pythagoras' Theorem

Once upon a time there lived a clever chap called Pythagoras. He came up with a clever theorem...

Pythagoras' Theorem is Used on Right Angled Triangles

PYTHAGORAS' THEOREM is a handy little formula for RIGHT-ANGLED TRIANGLES. What it does is let you find the length of the third side when you know two of them.

The formula for Pythagoras' theorem is: $a^2 + b^2 = h^2$ where a and b are the short sides and h is the long side of the triangle (called the hypotenuse)

Remember that Pythagoras can only be used on RIGHT-ANGLED TRIANGLES.

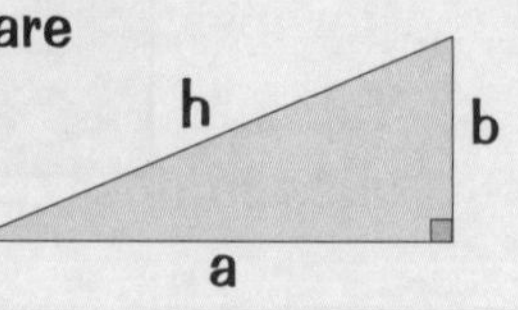

The trouble is, the formula can be quite difficult to use. Instead, it's a lot better to just remember these three simple steps, which work every time:

Calculator buttons are covered on p8-9, you need to know them all for Unit 3 so flick back.

1) Square Them

SQUARE THE TWO NUMBERS that you are given, (use the x^2 button if you've got your calculator.)

2) Add or Subtract

To find the longest side, ADD the two squared numbers. To find a shorter side, SUBTRACT the smaller one from the larger.

3) Square Root

Once you've got your answer, take the SQUARE ROOT (use the √ button on your calculator).

EXAMPLE 1: "Find the missing side in the triangle shown."

1) Square them: $5^2 = 25$, $3^2 = 9$
2) You want to find a shorter side, so SUBTRACT: $25 - 9 = 16$
3) Square root: $\sqrt{16} = 4$
   So the missing side = 4 m

5m
3m
?

(You should always ask yourself: "Is it a *sensible answer?*" — in this case you can say "YES, because it's shorter than 5 m, as it should be since 5 m is the longest side, but not too much shorter")

EXAMPLE 2: "Find the length of the line segment shown."

1) Work out how far across and up it is from A to B
2) Treat this exactly like a normal triangle...
3) Square them: $3^2 = 9$, $4^2 = 16$
4) You want to find the longest side (the hypotenuse), so ADD: $9 + 16 = 25$
5) Square root: $\sqrt{25} = 5$
   So the length of the line segment = 5 units

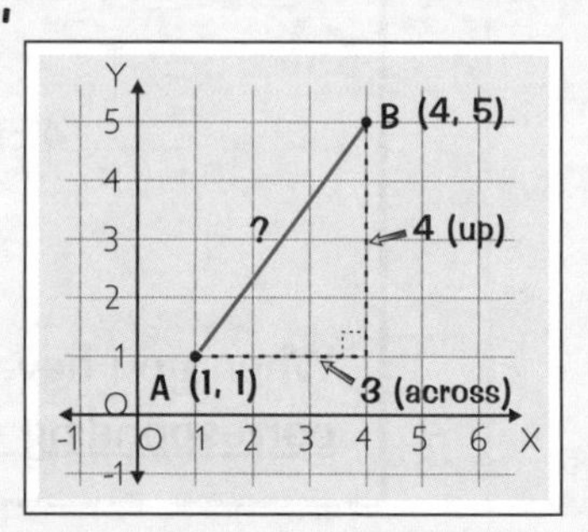

Hurrah, huzzah and all things joyful — triangles are the best...

...or is that just me... Anyway, you need to know this page, so test yourself with these:

1) Apply the above method to find the missing side BC:
2) Another triangle has sides of 5 m, 12 m and 13 m. Is it a right-angled triangle? How do you know?

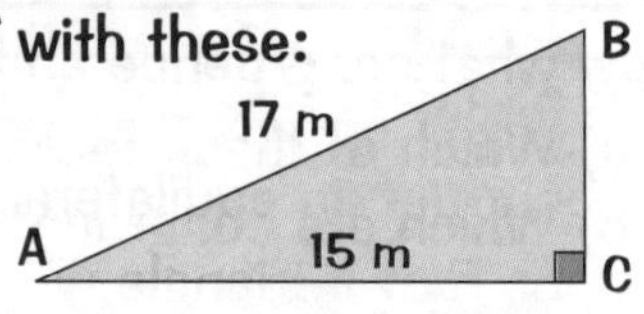

Drawing Shapes

I just know that you're dying to draw some shapes about now. And that's so weird, because that's exactly what's coming up next in this uber-exciting quest to master GCSE maths. Spooky.

You Need to be Able to Use Compasses, Rulers and Protractors

1) If you're asked to draw a shape accurately you'll be given the lengths, the angles, or both.
2) All you need to do then is use your ruler (for measuring out lengths), your protractor (for measuring out angles) or a pair of compasses (for drawing circles or arcs — see below).
3) You could get asked to draw circles, quadrilaterals or triangles. Triangles are the trickiest ones to do, but fret not, here are some examples to help you out:

Constructing a Triangle

Example: Construct the triangle ABC where AB = 6 cm, BC = 4 cm, AC = 5 cm.

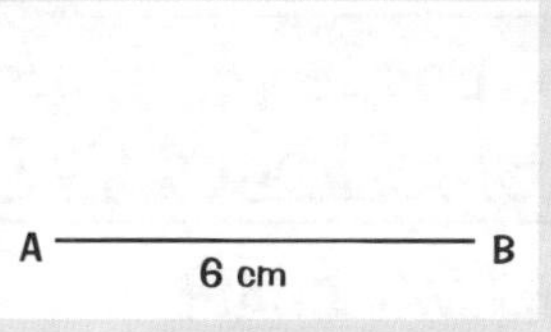

Pick a side for the base line — it doesn't matter which one. We'll pick AB. Draw a line 6 cm long. Label the ends A and B.

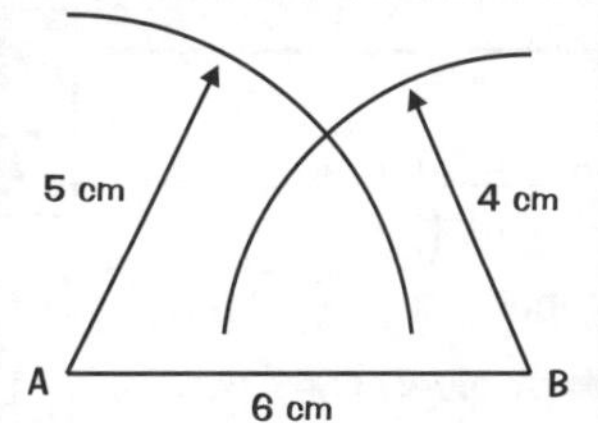

For AC, set the compasses to 5 cm, put the point at A and draw an arc. For BC, set the compasses to 4 cm, put the point at B and draw an arc.

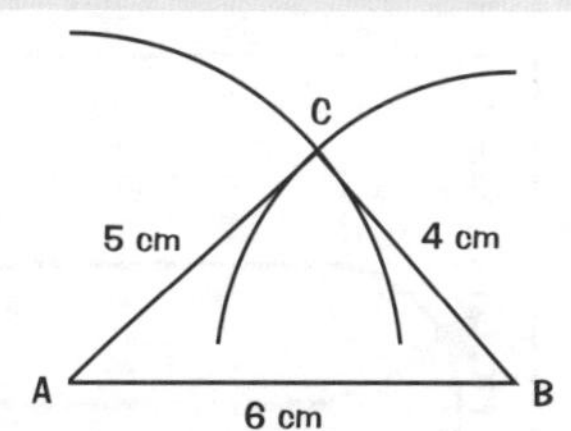

Where the arcs cross is the point C. Draw a line from A to C and another line from B to C to finish your triangle.

Example: Construct the triangle DEF where DE = 5cm, DF = 3cm, and angle EDF = 40°

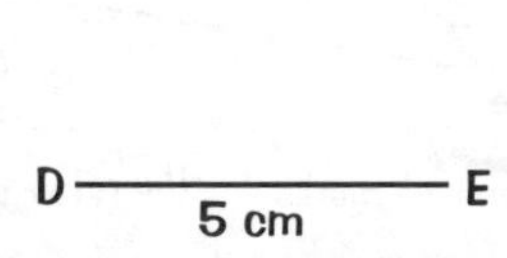

Pick a side for the base line — again, it doesn't matter which one. I've picked DE. Draw a line 5cm long. Label the ends D and E.

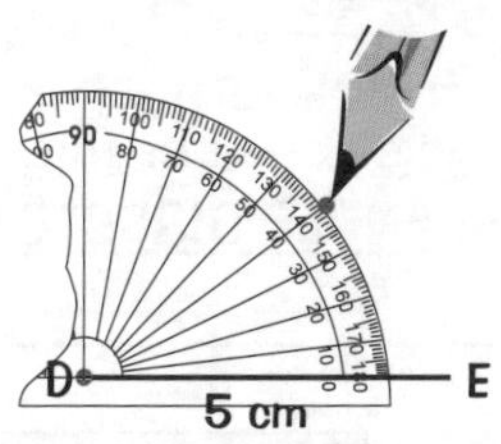

Next you have to draw the angle EDF (the angle at D): Place the centre of the protractor over D, measure 40° and put a dot.

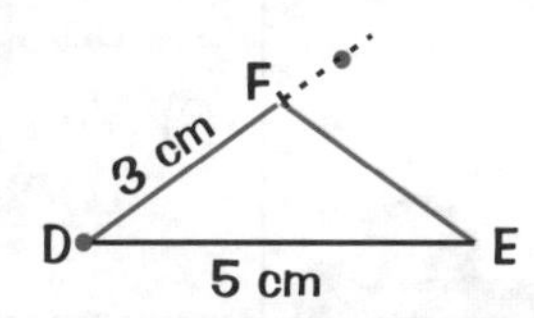

Measure 3 cm towards the dot and label it F. Draw a line from D to F. Now you've drawn the two sides and the angle. Just join up F and E to complete the triangle.

Compasses at the ready — three, two, one... Construct...

Don't forget to take a pencil, ruler and compasses into the exam. Or you'll look like a plonker.

1) Construct an equilateral triangle with sides 5 cm.
2) Construct a triangle with sides 3 cm, 4 cm and 5 cm. Check it by measuring the sides.

Loci and Constructions

"Loci and constructions — what the monkey is that about" I hear you cry. Well, wonder no more...

Drawing Loci

A **LOCUS** (another ridiculous maths word) is simply:

A LINE that shows all the points which fit in with a given rule

Make sure you learn how to do these **PROPERLY** using a **RULER AND COMPASSES** as shown.

The locus of points which are 'A fixed distance from a given point'

This locus is simply a **CIRCLE**.

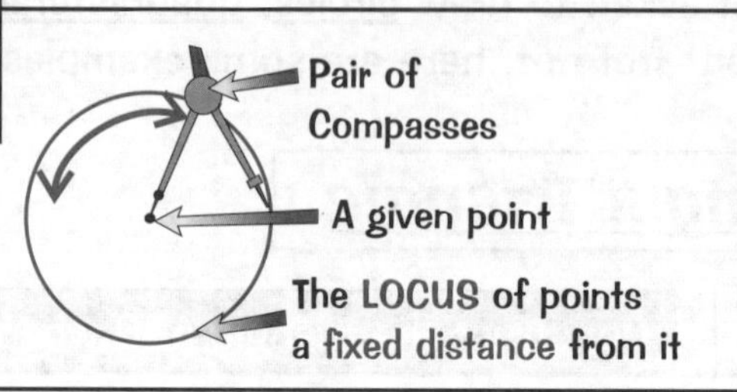

The locus of points which are 'A fixed distance from a given line'

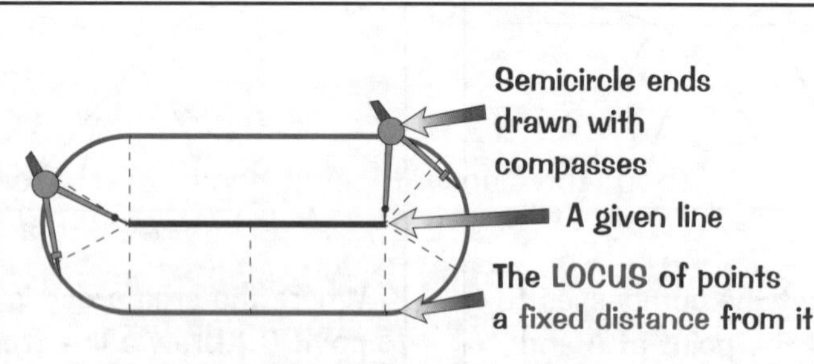

This locus is an **OVAL SHAPE**

It has straight sides (drawn with a ruler) and ends which are perfect semicircles (drawn with compasses).

The locus of points which are 'Equidistant from two given lines'

1) Keep the compass setting **THE SAME** while you make all four marks.
2) Make sure you leave your compass marks showing.
3) You get two equal angles — i.e. this **LOCUS** is actually an **ANGLE BISECTOR**.

Equidistant just means 'the same distance'.

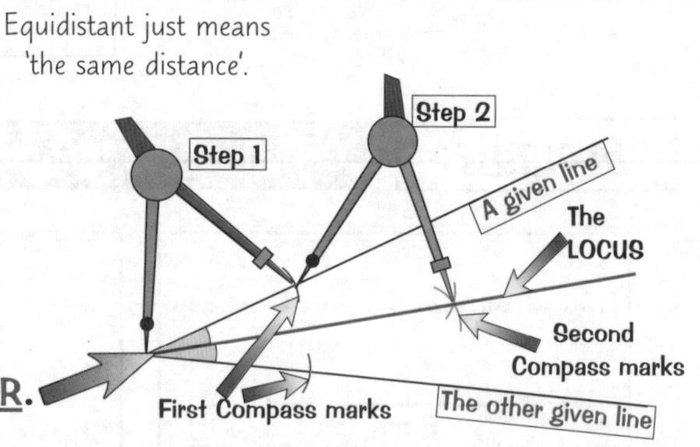

The locus of points which are 'Equidistant from two given POINTS'

Step 1
Step 1
Step 3
The LOCUS
A
B
Step 2
Step 2

(In the diagram above, A and B are the two given points)

This LOCUS is all the points which are the same distance from A and B.

This time the locus is actually the **PERPENDICULAR BISECTOR** of the line joining the two points.

Weird, scary, mutant monkey. Run... RUN...

Loci and Constructions

More on loci and constructions. Don't be alarmed by the floating, body-less hands. They're just there to point out the right diagram at the right time. Just pretend they're regular arrows.

Constructing accurate 60° and 30° angles

1) They may well ask you to draw an accurate 60° or 30° angle.
2) One place 60° angles are needed is for drawing an equilateral triangle.
3) Make sure you follow the method shown in this diagram, and that you can do it entirely from memory.
4) To draw a 30° angle just follow the same method and then bisect the 60° angle (see previous page).

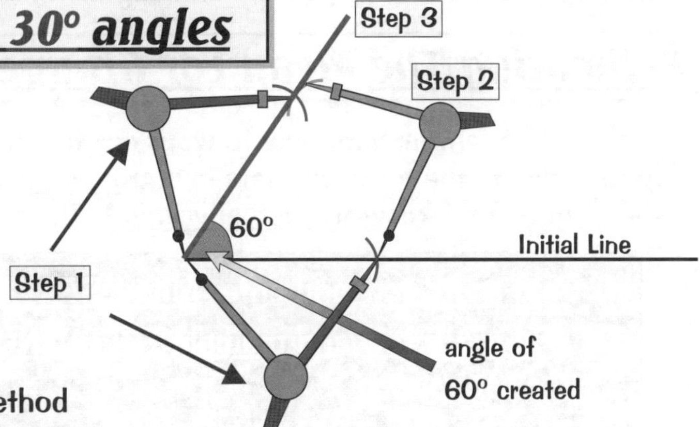

Constructing accurate 90° and 45° angles

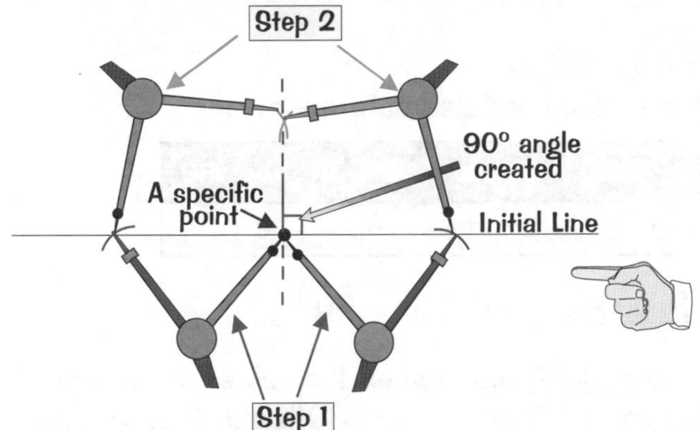

1) They might want you to draw an accurate 90° or 45° angle.
2) They won't accept it just done 'by eye' or with a ruler — if you want to get the marks, you've got to do it the proper way with compasses like I've shown you here.
3) Make sure you can follow the method shown in this diagram to draw 90° angles.
4) To draw 45° angles follow the same method and then bisect the 90° angle.

Drawing the Perpendicular from a Point to a Line

1) This is similar to the one above but not quite the same — make sure you can do both.
2) Again, they won't accept it just done 'by eye' or with a ruler — you've got to do it the proper way with compasses.
3) Learn the diagram.

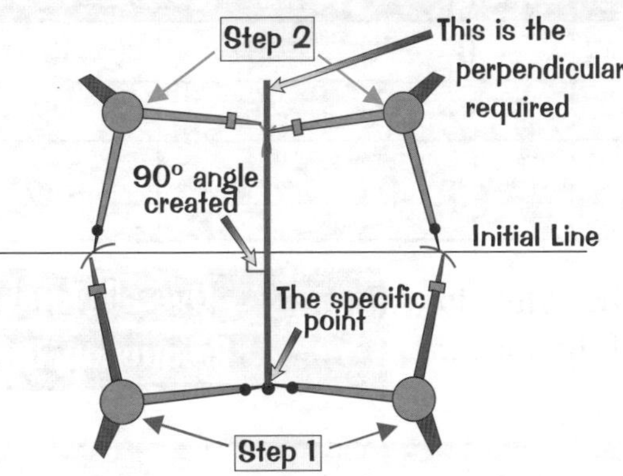

If you're loci, you won't get tested on this stuff...

Haha — I crack myself up. But hilarious jokes aside, make sure you do learn these pages. Start by covering them up and drawing an example of each of the four loci from memory. Then draw an equilateral triangle and a square, both with fabulously accurate 60° and 90° angles. Also, draw a line and a point and construct the perpendicular from the point to the line. Lovely.

Grouped Frequency Tables

Time to turn our attention to data handling now. "Hooray" I hear you yell in an enthusiastic manner. A lot of the basics are covered in Unit 1, but you need to know them here as well, so if your memory of frequency tables and averages is a bit hazy then flick back to p.33-36 before launching into this stuff.

Estimating The Mean For Grouped Data

You should be familiar with how to work out the mean of a set of numbers. But you also need to be able to estimate the mean for data in a grouped frequency table. (You can only estimate the mean because you don't know the actual values.) The method is easy once you've learnt it:

1) Add a 3rd row and enter MID-INTERVAL VALUES for each group.
2) Add a 4th row and multiply FREQUENCY × MID-INTERVAL VALUE for each group.
3) Work out the TOTALS of rows 2 and 4.
4) Get the mean by dividing ROW 4 TOTAL by ROW 2 TOTAL.

To find the mid-interval value, you just add together the upper and lower limits and divide by 2.

Example:

The table below shows the distribution of weights of 60 children.
Find the modal class, identify the class containing the median and estimate the mean.

Weight (kg)	$30 \le w < 40$	$40 \le w < 50$	$50 \le w < 60$	$60 \le w < 70$	$70 \le w < 80$
Frequency	8	16	18	12	6

1) The modal class is just the one with the highest frequency: $50 \le w < 60$ kg

2) The class containing the median is the one with the middle value (when the values are arranged in size order). There are 60 children, so the median value is between the 30th and 31st values.
So the class containing the median is: $50 \le w < 60$ kg (it contains the 25th to the 42nd value).

3) To find the mean, add two rows to the table as described above:

Weight (kg)	$30 \le w < 40$	$40 \le w < 50$	$50 \le w < 60$	$60 \le w < 70$	$70 \le w < 80$	Totals
Frequency	8	16	18	12	6	60
Mid-Interval Value	35	45	55	65	75	—
Frequency × Mid-Interval Value	280	720	990	780	450	3220

Now, just divide the totals to get an estimate of the mean:

$$\text{Mean} = \frac{\text{Overall Total (Final Row)}}{\text{Frequency Total (2nd Row)}} = \frac{3220}{60} = \underline{53.7}$$

This page auditioned for Britain's next top modal...

It didn't get through — but I think I'll try again next year. Learn all the stuff on this page, then turn over and write down everything you've just learned. Good, clean fun. Then have a go at these...

1) Estimate the mean for this table: 2) State the modal class.

Length L (cm)	$15.5 \le L < 16.5$	$16.5 \le L < 17.5$	$17.5 \le L < 18.5$	$18.5 \le L < 19.5$
Frequency	12	18	23	8

Grouped Frequency Graphs

Moving seamlessly on from grouped frequency tables to grouped frequency graphs.
What could be better... No wait, don't answer that...

Grouped Frequency Diagrams Show Grouped Data

Data that's been grouped can be shown in a grouped frequency diagram. These diagrams have a continuous scale along the x-axis and the frequency of each class is shown by bars. There are no gaps between the bars.

EXAMPLE The data below shows the number of slugs of different lengths found in a school.

Length of Slug (mm)	Frequency
$0 < L \leq 10$	30
$10 < L \leq 20$	70
$20 < L \leq 30$	110
$30 < L \leq 40$	100
$40 < L \leq 50$	80
$50 < L \leq 60$	20

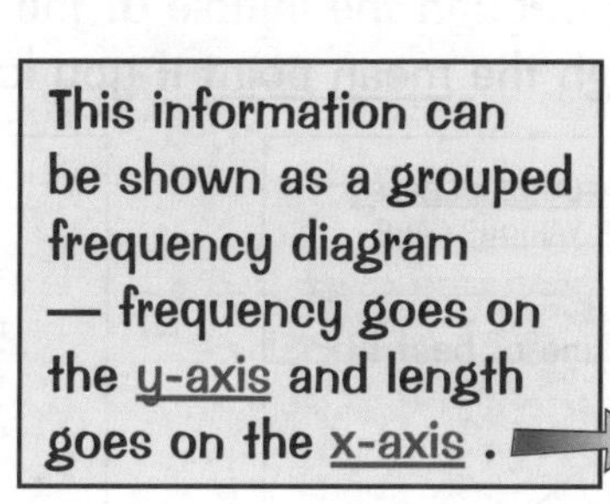
This information can be shown as a grouped frequency diagram — frequency goes on the y-axis and length goes on the x-axis.

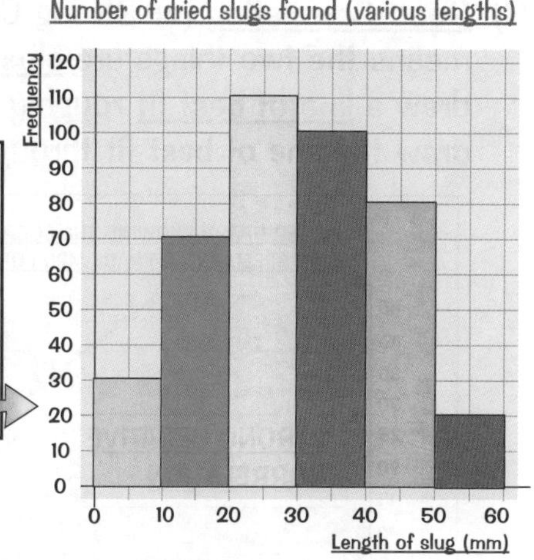

A Frequency Polygon Uses the Midpoint of Each Class

Frequency polygons can also be used to display grouped data:

EXAMPLE The frequency table below shows the heights of 12 plants in a biology experiment.

Height	$0 \leq h < 5$	$5 \leq h < 10$	$10 \leq h < 15$	$15 \leq h < 20$
Frequency	3	5	2	2

1) To show this on a frequency polygon you need to work out the MIDPOINTS for each class of heights first:

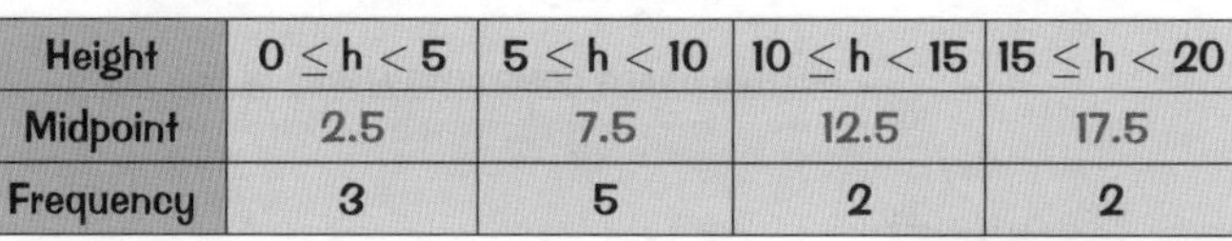

Height	$0 \leq h < 5$	$5 \leq h < 10$	$10 \leq h < 15$	$15 \leq h < 20$
Midpoint	2.5	7.5	12.5	17.5
Frequency	3	5	2	2

2) Then plot the midpoint of each class against frequency and join the points with straight lines.

The highest peak tells you the group with the highest frequency — 5-10 cm class.

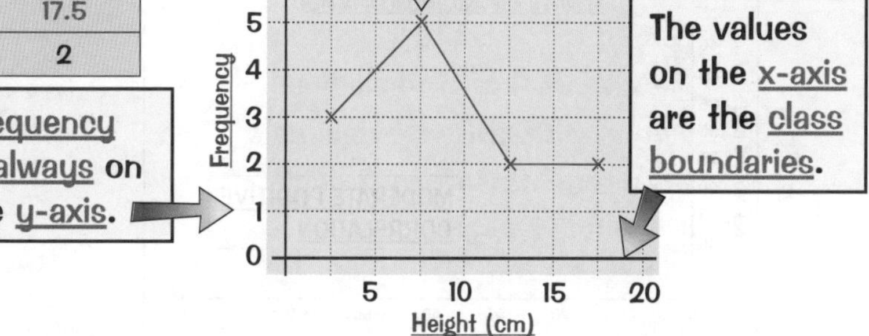

The values on the x-axis are the class boundaries.

The frequency of graphs in exams is pretty high...

...so you really do need to learn the stuff on this page. Which hopefully won't be too tricky. Just learn what a grouped frequency diagram is (it's really important that you remember there are no gaps between the bars), and how to draw a frequency polygon. If you can get your head around those two then you shouldn't have too many problems in the exam.

Scatter Graphs

You use a scatter graph to show how two different types of data (like height and weight) are related to each other. And as if by magic, there are some examples below.

Scatter Graphs

1) A SCATTER GRAPH is just a load of points on a graph that end up in a bit of a mess rather than in a nice line or curve.
2) There is a posh word to say how much of a mess they are in — it's CORRELATION.
3) Good Correlation (or Strong Correlation) means the points form quite a nice line, and it means the two things are closely related to each other. When this is the case, you can draw a line of best fit roughly through the middle of the scatter of points. You should draw the line of best fit through the mean point if you know where it is.

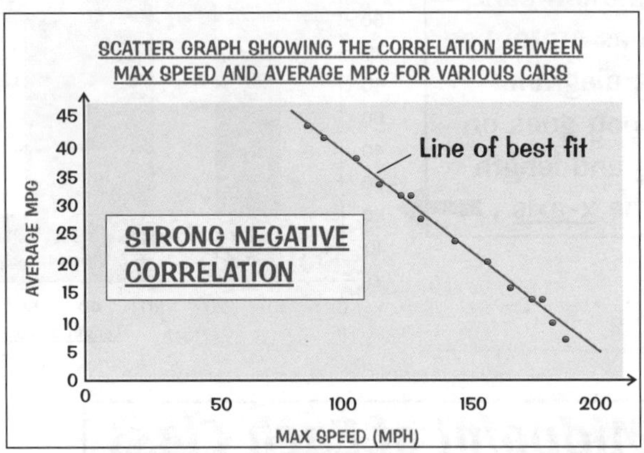

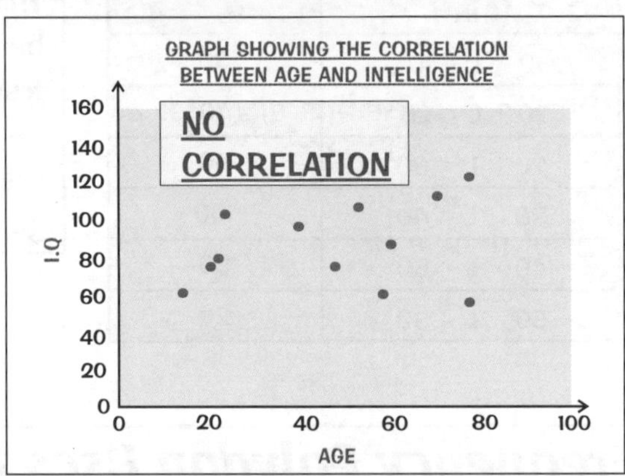

4) No Correlation means the points are all over the place and so there is no relation between the two things.
5) If the points form a line sloping UPHILL from left to right, then there is POSITIVE CORRELATION, which just means that both things increase or decrease together.
6) If the points form a line sloping DOWNHILL from left to right, then there is NEGATIVE CORRELATION, which just means that as one thing increases the other decreases.
7) So when you're describing a scatter graph you have to mention both things, i.e. whether it's strong/weak/moderate correlation and whether it's positive/negative.

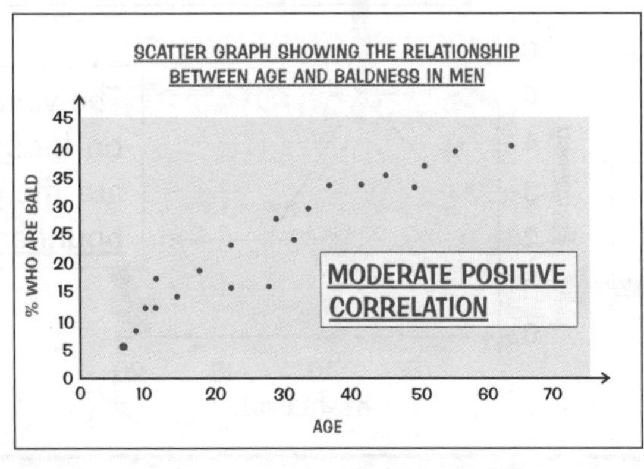

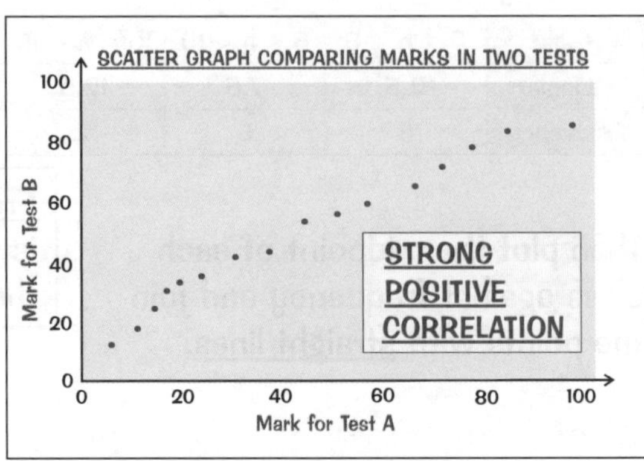

What soap do maths teachers watch — Correlation Street...

Recent studies have shown that there is strong positive correlation between time spent practising your evil laugh / cat stroking / beard combing and how successful you are as an evil genius. Learn all the charts on these two pages and have a go at drawing an example of each.

Revision Summary for Unit Three — 2

HURRAH — IT'S THE END OF THE BOOK. What you need here is some questions to check that you've learned everything you need to for the exam. Oh look, what's this I see...

1) Work out the exterior and interior angles for a regular octagon (8 sides).

2) A museum has a flight of stairs up to its front door (see diagram). A ramp is to be put over the top of the stairs for wheelchair users. Calculate the length that the ramp would need to be.

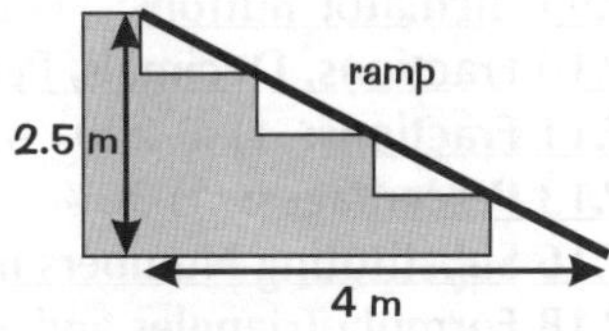

3) Construct a triangle ABC with sides AB = 9 cm, AC = 10 cm and BC = 8 cm.

4) Draw a circle with a diameter of 6 cm.

5) What is a locus? Describe in detail the four types you should know. Also, draw a 60° angle and a 90° angle using the proper methods.

6) Calum is writing an article on the Skelly Crag half-marathon for the local paper. He wants to include the average time taken. Use the times of all 1000 runners, recorded in the table below, to work out the mean time taken.

Time (min)	$60 < t \le 90$	$90 < t \le 120$	$120 < t \le 150$	$150 < t \le 180$	$180 < t \le 210$	$210 < t \le 240$
Frequency	15	60	351	285	206	83

7) A newspaper has claimed that a study shows a strong positive correlation between eating cheese and having nightmares. The results of the study are shown on the right.
a) What does strong positive correlation mean?
b) Do you agree with the newspaper claim?

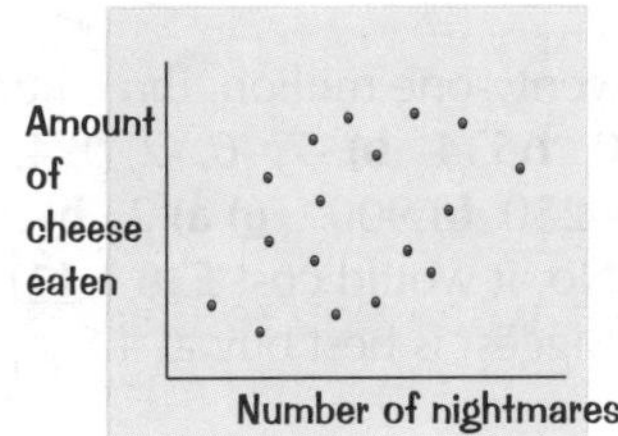

Aaarrrggghhh...
Run FASTER...

Answers

Unit One

P.4 Big Numbers: 1) a) One million, two hundred and thirty-four thousand, five hundred and thirty-one **b)** Twenty-three thousand, four hundred and fifty-six **c)** Two thousand, four hundred and fifteen **d)** Three thousand, four hundred and two **e)** Two hundred and three thousand, four hundred and twelve **2)** 56,421 **3)** 9, 23, 87, 345, 493, 1029, 3004 **4)** 2, 8, 9, 37, 307
P.6 Rounding Off: 1) a) 3.2 **b)** 1.8 **c)** 2.3 **d)** 0.5 **e)** 9.8 **2) a)** 3.47 **b)** 5.28 **c)** 1.84 **d)** 6.96 **e)** 3.27
P.7 Rounding Off: 1) a) 450 **b)** 680 **c)** 50 **d)** 100 **e)** 10 **2) a)** 350 **b)** 500 **c)** 12.4 **d)** 0.036
P.9 Calculator Buttons: 1) a) 1.70 **b)** 39.96
P.10 Fractions, Decimals, Percentages and Ratios: 1) a) 0.3 **b)** 4/5 or 8/10
P.11 Fractions: 1) a) 220 **b)** £1.75 **c)** £5
P.13 Percentages: 1) 30%
P.16 Substituting Numbers into Formulas: 1) £14
P.18 Formula Triangles and Speed: 1) Speed = Distance ÷ Time **2)** Time = 7½ hrs Dist = 11.2 km
P.21 Metric and Imperial Units: 1) a) 200 **b)** 65 **2) a)** 2.5 **b)** 1.5 **3)** 3 feet 10 inches **4) a)** 200 or 220 yards **b)** 187.5 cm
P.24 Measuring and Drawing Angles: 1) See P.24 **2)** see angles on right.
P.26 Bearings: 1) See right.
P.27 Perimeters: 2) 42cm.
P.29 Areas: 1) 12 cm² **2)** 12 m² **3)** 21 m² **4)** 78 cm²
P.30 Volume: a) $V = 148.5 \text{ cm}^3$ **b)** $V = 0.70 \text{ m}^3$ or $700\,000 \text{ cm}^3$
P.31 Clock Time Questions: 1) 5:15pm **2)** 4:05pm **3)** 1,440 ; 86,400 **4)** 3hrs 30 min; 5hrs 45 min
P.34 Grouped Frequency Tables: 1) a) Discrete, possible table: Columns "Shoe Size" and "frequency", Shoe size intervals: 3, 4, 5, 6, 7, 8, 9, 10 , 11, 12 **b)** Continuous, possible table: Columns "Height (cm)" and "frequency", intervals: $140 \le h < 150$, $150 \le h < 160$, $160 \le h < 170$, etc.
P.35 Mean, Median, Mode and Range: First, do this: -14, -12, -5, -5, 0, 1, 3, 6, 7, 8, 10, 14, 18, 23, 25 Mean = 5.27, Median = 6, Mode = -5, Range = 39
P.38 Charts and Graphs: See pie chart to the right.

Revision Summary for Unit One — 1 (p.20)

1) Twenty-one million, three hundred and six thousand, five hundred and fifteen. **2) a)** 2, 23, 45, 123, 132, 789, 2200, 6534 **b)** -7, -6, -2, 0, 4, 5, 8, 10 **3) a)** 1 **b)** 3 **c)** 16 **d)** 12 **4) a)** 5.3 **b)** 3.5 **c)** 6.2 **5) a)** 250 **b)** 900 **6) a)** 2 **b)** 2 **c)** 1 **d)** 3 **e)** 2 **7)** 4/5 **8) a)** 320 **b)** £60 **c)** 195 **9)** £58.75 **10)** No, it would cost £36 **11) a)** £2040.73 **b)** £2100 **12)** Golden Rule: "DIVIDE BY THE PRICE IN PENCE" **13)** Biggest is best buy at 4.8 g per penny **14)** £1740 **15)** 1:15 pm

Revision Summary for Unit One — 2 (p.40)

1) No **2)** See P.22 **3)** £20.63 **4)** Yes **5)** 17 miles **6)** 65.45 kg **7)** See right **8)** 28 m **9)** £1008 **10)** E.g. a cuboid measuring 3 cm by 2 cm by 5 cm **11)** 12.50pm **12)** 21:25 **13)** Values of w from 50 to 60 **including** 50, but **not including** 60. 60 would go in the next group up. **14)** First put in order: 2, 3, 4, 6, 7, 7, 12, 15 **a)** 7 **b)** 6.5 **c)** 7 **d)** 13 **15) a)** Angles are: Blue 108°, Red 135°, Yellow 36°, White 81° **b)** See pie chart.

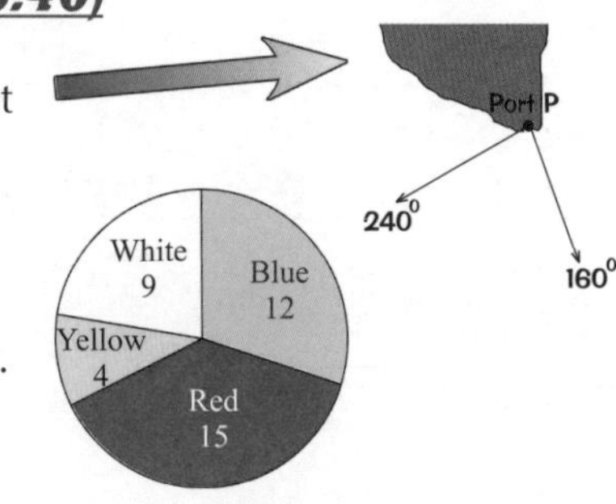

Unit Two

P.41 Multiplying by 10, 100, etc: 1) a) 1230 **b)** 3450 **c)** 9650 **2) a)** 48 **b)** 450 **c)** 180 000
P.42 Dividing by 10, 100, etc: 1) a) 0.245 **b)** 6.542 **c)** 0.00308 **2) a)** 1.6 **b)** 12 **c)** 5
P.43 Addition and Subtraction: 1) a) 171 cm, **b)** 19 cm **2)** 1.72 litres
P.45 Dividing Without a Calculator: 1) 336 **2)** 616 **3)** 832 **4)** 12 **5)** 121 **6)** 12 **7)** 179.2 **8)** 56 **9)** 46 **10)** 12

Answers

P.46 Special Number Sequences: 1) EVENS: 2, 4, 6, 8, 10, 12, 14, 16, 18, 20, 22, 24, 26, 28, 30
ODDS: 1, 3, 5, 7, 9, 11, 13, 15, 17, 19, 21, 23, 25, 27, 29
SQUARES: 1, 4, 9, 16, 25, 36, 49, 64, 81, 100, 121, 144, 169, 196, 225
CUBES: 1, 8, 27, 64, 125, 216, 343, 512, 729, 1000, 1331, 1728, 2197, 2744, 3375
POWERS OF 2: 2, 4, 8, 16, 32, 64, 128, 256, 512, 1024, 2048, 4096, 8192, 16384, 32768;
POWERS OF 10: 10, 100, 1000, 10 000, 100 000, 1 000 000, 10 000 000, 100 000 000, 1 000 000 000, 10 000 000 000, 100 000 000 000, 1 000 000 000 000, 10 000 000 000 000, 100 000 000 000 000, 1 000 000 000 000 000 hmm...
2) a) 56, 134, 156, 36, 64 **b)** 23, 45, 81, 25, 97, 125, 1 **c)** 81, 25, 36, 1, 64 **d)** 125, 1, 64 **e)** 1, 64

P.47 Prime Numbers: 1) 2, 3, 5, 7, 11, 13, 17, 19, 23, 29, 31, 37, 41, 43, 47 **2)** 97, 101, 103, 107, 109

P.48 Multiples, Factors and Prime Factors: 1) 7, 14, 21, 28, 35, 42, 49, 56, 63, 70 and 9, 18, 27, 36, 45, 54, 63, 72, 81, 90 **2)** 1, 2, 3, 4, 6, 9, 12, 18, 36 and 1, 2, 3, 4, 6, 7, 12, 14, 21, 28, 42, 84
3) a) $990 = 2\times3\times3\times5\times11$ **b)** $160 = 2\times2\times2\times2\times2\times5$

P.49 LCM and HCF: 1) 8, 16, 24, 32, 40, 48, 56, 64, 72, 80 and 9, 18, 27, 36, 45, 54, 63, 72, 81, 90 LCM = 72 **2)** 1, 2, 4, 7, 8, 14, 28, 56 and 1, 2, 4, 8, 13, 26, 52, 104 HCF = 8 **3)** 63 **4)** 12

P.50 Powers: 1) a) 3^8 **b)** 4 **c)** 8^{12} **d)** 1 **e)** 7^6 **2) a)** 5^{12} **b)** 2^5

P.51 Roots and Reciprocals: 1) a) g = 6 or -6 **b)** b = 4 **c)** r = 3 or -3 **d)** r = 1/2

P.52 Fractions, Decimals and Percentages: 1) a) 6/10 = 3/5 **b)** 2/100 = 1/50 **c)** 77/100 **d)** 555/1000 = 111/200 **e)** 56/10 = 28/5 or 5 3/5

P.53 Fractions, Decimals and Percentages: 1) 3/5, 2/3, 11/15 **2)** 23%, 3/12, 47%, 6/8

P.54 Fractions and Estimating Calculations: 1) a) 5/32 **b)** 32/35 **c)** 23/20 = 1 3/20 **d)** 1/40 **e)** 167/27 = 6 5/27 **2)** 10

P.55 X and Y Coordinates: A(4,5) B(6,0) C(5,-5) D(0,-3) E(-5,-2) F(-4,0) G(-3,3) H(0,5)

P.56 Midpoint of a Line Segment: 1) (3,5) **2)** (5,1)

P.58 Straight Line Graphs: 1) And **2)**

x	-4	-2	-1	0	1	2	4
y	-6	-4	-3	-2	-1	0	2

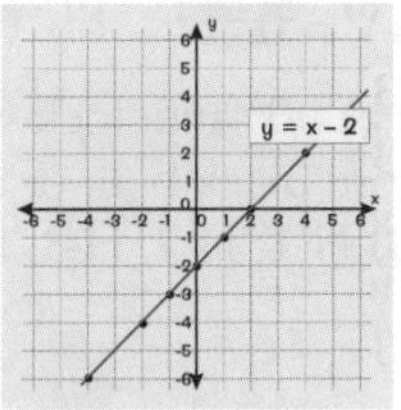

P.59 Straight Line Graphs — Gradients: Gradient = -1.5

P.60 Straight Line Graphs — y = mx + c: 1) y = 4 − 2x, y = x − 3 **2)** a) y = 2 − ½x b) y = x + 3 c) y = 6 − 2x

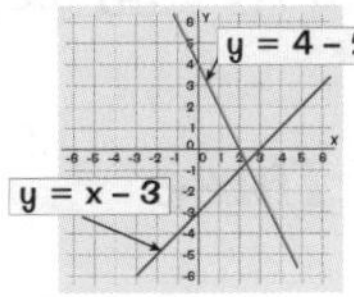

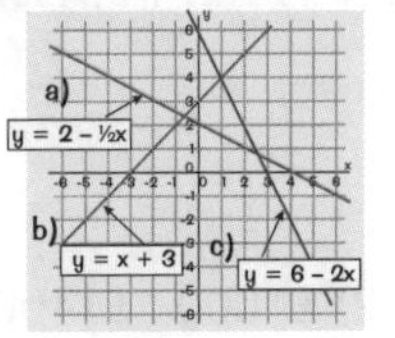

P.61 Quadratic and Cubic Graphs: 1) a) x^2 bucket shape **b)** $-x^3$ wiggle (top left to bottom right)

P.62 Quadratic and Cubic Graphs: Using graph, solutions are x = -2 and x = 3.

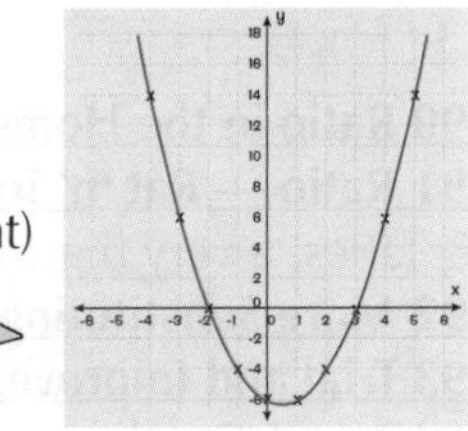

P.63 Algebra: 1) a) $4x + y - 4$ **b)** $9x + 5xy - 5$ **c)** $5x + 3x^2 + 5y^2$ **d)** $6y - 4xy$
2) a) +18 **b)** -216 **c)** 2 **d)** -27 **e)** -336

P.64 Algebra: 1) a) $2x - 4$ **b)** $5x + x^2$ **c)** $y^2 + xy$ **d)** $6xy - 18y$ **2) a)** $5x(y + 3)$ **b)** $a(5 - 7b)$ **c)** $6y(2x + 1 - 6y)$

P.66 Number Patterns and Sequences: 1) a) 20, 27 "Add one extra each time" **b)** 2000 20 000 "Multiply the previous term by 10" **c)** 4, 2 "Divide the previous term by 2" **2)** 2n + 5

P.67 Solving Equations: 1) x = 8 **2)** x = 7

P.68 Solving Equations: 1) a) x = 4 **b)** q = 32 **c)** y = -2 **2)** b = ½a + 3

P.69 Inequalities: 1) $x \geqslant -2$ **2)** $x \geqslant -4$, $x < 2$, x = -4, -3, -2, -1, 0, 1

P.72 Symmetry: H : 2 lines of symmetry, Rot^n symmetry Order 2,
Z : 0 lines of symmetry, Rot^n symmetry Order 2,
N : 0 lines of symmetry, Rot^n symmetry Order 2,
× **:** 4 lines of symmetry, Rot^n symmetry Order 4,
T : 1 line of symmetry, No Rotational symmetry,
E : 1 line of symmetry, No Rotational symmetry,
S : 0 lines of symmetry, Rot^n symmetry Order 2

P.77 Lines and Angles: 1) Actual angles given — accept answers within 10°: **a)** 36° **b)** 79° **c)** 162° **d)** 287°

P.79 Parallel Lines: See right

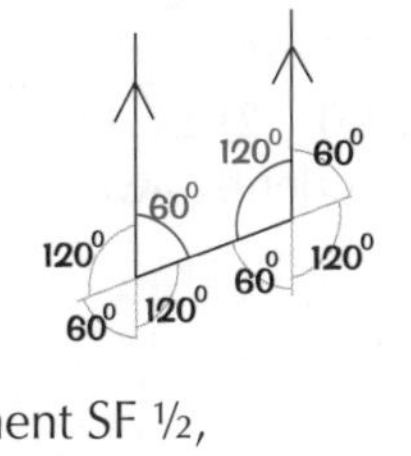

120° 60° 60° 120° 120° 60° 60° 120°

P.81 The Four Transformations: 1) A → B Rotation ¼ turn clockwise about the origin. B → C reflection in the line y=x. C → A reflection in the y-axis. A → D translation of 9 left and 7 down

P.83 Enlargements: 1) 2430 cm^2 **2)** 1875 cm^3

P.84 Combinations of Transformations: 1) C→D, Reflection in the y-axis, and an enlargement SF 2, centre the origin, **D→C**, Reflection in the y-axis, and an enlargement SF ½, centre the origin. **2) A′→B**, Rotation of 180° clockwise or anticlockwise about the point (0,3).

P.85 Probability: 1) 1/13

P.86 Probability: 1) 1/5 or 20% or 0.2

P.87 Probability: 1) a) Probability = QJ = (4/52)(4/51) = 4/663 **b)** Probability = (13/52)(12/51) = 39/663 = 1/17

P.88 Probablility — Relative Frequency: 1) Landing on red: 0.43, landing on blue: 0.24, landing on green: 0.33

Answers

Revision Summary for Unit Two — 1 (P.70)

1) £120 2) 32p 3) 50p 4) **a)** £7.16 **b)** 5.87 5) **a)** 224 **b)** 54 6) See P.46 7) 41, 43, 47, 53, 59 8) Multiples are a number's times table; 10, 20, 30, 40, 50, 60; 4, 8, 12, 16, 20, 24;
9) **a)** $210 = 2 \times 3 \times 5 \times 7$ **b)** $1050 = 2 \times 3 \times 5 \times 5 \times 7$ 10) 40 11) **a)** 1296 **b)** 16
12) **a)** +16, –16 **b)** 6 13) 645/1000 = 129/200 14) **a)** 88/30 = 44/15 = $2\frac{14}{15}$ **b)** 75/48 = 25/16 = $1\frac{9}{16}$
c) 23/8 = $2\frac{7}{8}$ **d)** 11/21 15) 10 16) **a)** It's a hit, so yes, he's cheating. **b)** Yes
17) See right 18) **a)** straight line **b)** quadratic **c)** straight line **d)** quadratic
19) 5x 20) 12g + 20h – 4 21) 2x(1 + 3y)
22) **a)** 19, 23; add 4 to the previous term
b) 6, 3; subtract one less each time 23) nth number = 4n – 3
24) y = 2x + 4 25) **a)** y = 6 – x **b)** y = (x – 11) / 2 **c)** y = 3(7x + 3) or y = 21x + 9
26) **a)** x < 5 **b)** x < -1 **c)** x > -5 **d)** x > 10

x	-5	-3	-1	0	1	2	4	6
y	-2	0	2	3	4	5	7	9

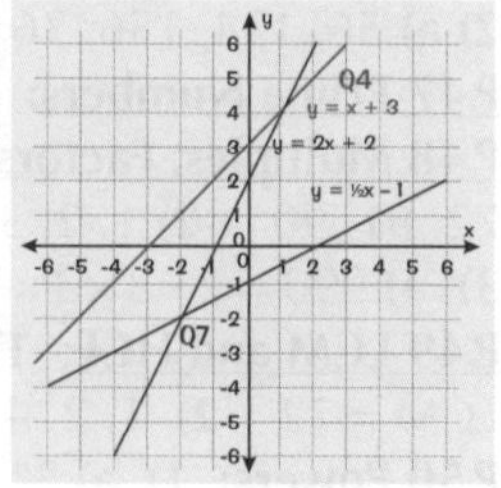

Revision Summary for Unit Two — 2 (P.89)

1) Line Symmetry, Plane Symmetry and Rotational Symmetry 2) **a)** **b)** 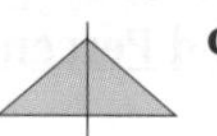 **c)** 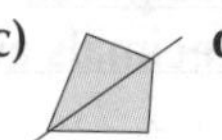 **d)** 
3) 6 m 4) See page 74

5) **a)** **b)** 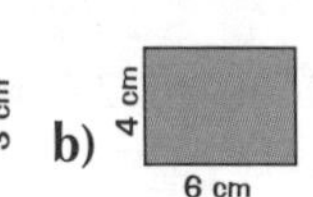 **c)** 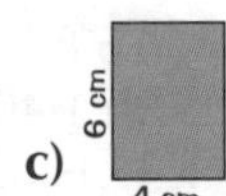 6) See page 76 7) See top of P.77 8) X = 110°, Y = 40°

9) **a)** 90° anticlockwise rotation about the origin **b)** Reflection in the line y = 1 10) 3 11) **a)** 53.3% **b)** Add one more black ball, or take away one red or one green ball. 12) H-H, H-T, T-H, T-T ¼
13) H-1, H-2, H-3, H-4, H-5, H-6, T-1, T-2, T-3, T-4, T-5, T-6 $\frac{1}{12}$ 14) 0.8

Unit Three

P.90 Ratio in the Home: 1) 56p 2) £1000 : £1400
P.91 Ratio — Rat 'n' Toad Pie: Recipe for 9: 9 rats, 4.5 toads, 11.25 Oz of "Froggatt's Lumpy Sprout Ketchup", 18 'taties, a very big wodge of pastry (2.25 times as big as for 4 people in fact)
P.92 More Substituting into Formulas: 2) 25
P.93 Trial and Improvement: x = 1.6
P.94 Travel Graphs, Speed and Density: 1) Density = Mass ÷ Volume 2) 16.5 g/cm³ 3) 603 g
P.96 Polygons and Estimating Areas: 1) Ext. angle = 72°, Int. angle = 108° 2) Ext. angle = 30°, Int. angle = 150° 3) 3cm²
P.97 Congruence and Similarity: 1) **a)** i, ii and iv are similar. **b)** i and ii are congruent.
P.98 Pythagoras' Theorem: 1) BC = 8 m, 2) 5 m, 12 m, 13 m is a right angled triangle because $a^2 + b^2 = h^2$ works.
P.102 Grouped Frequency Tables: (See table on right)
1) Mean ≈ 17.4 cm 2) Modal Class = 17.5 ≤ L < 18.5

Length L (cm)	15.5 ≤ L < 16.5	16.5 ≤ L < 17.5	17.5 ≤ L < 18.5	18.5 ≤ L < 19.5	Totals
Frequency	12	18	23	8	61
Mid-Interval Value	16	17	18	19	—
Freq × MIV	192	306	414	152	1064

Revision Summary for Unit Three — 1 (P.95)

1) See P.90 2) £1.41 3) 240 4) **a)** $F = \frac{9}{5}C + 32$ **b)** $F = \frac{9}{5}(30) + 32 = 86$ °F 5) x = 5.5 to 1 d.p.
6) **a)** Wandering away from home. **b)** Stood still chomping grass. **c)** 2½ km 7) 29 000 cm³

Revision Summary for Unit Three — 2 (P.105)

1) 45° and 135° 2) 4.72 m 3) Measure all sides to check it's right. 4) Measure the diameter to check it's right.
5) See p100-101 6) Mean ≈ ((75 × 15) + (105 × 60) + (135 × 351) + (165 × 285) + (195 × 206) + (225 × 83)) ÷ 1000 = 160 680 ÷ 1000 = 161 min 7) **a)** Both things increase or decrease together and they're closely related. (The more cheese you eat, the more you tend to have nightmares.) **b)** No, the graph shows very weak correlation.

Index

Index